CW00546133

WILD BOAR
IN BRITAIN

WILD BOAR
IN BRITAIN

Martin Goulding

Whittet Books

For Molly Rose

A wild boar stood under a tree and rubbed his tusks against the trunk. A fox passing by asked him why he thus sharpened his teeth when there was no danger threatening from either huntsman or hound. He replied, 'I do it advisedly; for it would never do to have to sharpen my weapons just at the time I ought to be using them.'

Aesop's Fables 'The wild boar and the fox'

First published 2003
Text © 2003 by Martin Goulding
This new edition published 2008
Whittet Books Ltd, South House, Yatesbury Manor, Yatesbury, Wiltshire SN11 8YE

Line drawings by Louise Fenton
Photographs by the author unless otherwise stated

Cataloguing in Publication Data
A catalogue record for this title is available from the British Library

ISBN-13 978-1-873580-58-5

Printed and bound in Britain by Cromwell Press

Contents

Preface

I am sitting in a tree, in a wood, in southern England. My clothes mimic the green and brown hues of the woodland. I have a scarf wrapped around my face and a cap pulled tightly down over my eyes. My field of vision is similar to looking out from inside a pillar-box. I have been in this tree for over an hour trying not to fidget or change position too often. The animals I have come to watch, despite their fearsome reputation, are nervous and wary of people. They don't always show, making their eventual appearance all the more rewarding. The light is beginning to fade and a blackbird, looking for a place to roost, lands on a nearby branch. My camouflage does not fool him and he flies away emitting an alarm call that pierces the evening silence. Just then, into the clearing by my carefully selected tree, finally arrive the wild boar. Two sows, three juveniles and six striped piglets troop in single file out from the trees. I watch as they root amongst the leaf litter and listen to their communicative grunts and squeals. The piglets comically squabble amongst themselves and play-fight.

Wild boar became extinct in Britain several hundred years ago. Watching these animals below me, living freely again in their ancestral habitat, is exhilarating and a privilege. They are descendants of escaped farm stock and this woodland is one of their strongholds. A few minutes later the animals move off to forage elsewhere in the woodland and I climb down before it becomes too dark to see the branches below me. I walk to my vehicle parked a short distance away, glad to exercise stiff limbs. Behind me I hear the wild boar softly grunting amongst themselves as they move through the wood. I know they pose no physical threat but still I cannot help glancing over my shoulder and quickening my step. I drive out of the woodland and enter the brightly lit streets of the town. I see people going into bars and restaurants but I have had enough excitement for one evening, I have been watching wild boar.

My fascination with the return of these animals was shared by many others, but little information about the animals' biology and behaviour was available. The only books on the subject were written in the language of the countries where wild boar continue to live in numbers. More than once I regretted the lack of attention I paid during school language classes. I have now studied the free-living wild boar in Britain for over ten years and have plugged many of the gaps in my own knowledge. I have therefore written this book with the aim of increasing our awareness and understanding of this fascinating beast, which has honoured us with its presence once again.

Martin Goulding, 2008

1

CULTURE AND HERITAGE

A historical perspective

Six thousand years ago Britain was covered by vast tracts of woodland. More than one million wild boar are thought to have inhabited these wildwoods of oak, ash, lime and hazel. This was their finest hour. The sparse human population of the time roved the woodlands as hunter-gatherers, surviving on fish from the rivers and wild animals such as wild boar, deer, elk and aurochs (extinct wild cattle). Berries, nuts, cereals and wild flowers were gathered where they were found. No crops were grown and no livestock tended.

These primitive stone-age hunters were soon joined by waves of immigrants from several different races and tribes out of western and central Europe. They crossed the seas in dug-out canoes, wicker coracles and small skin boats. These early Celts came from more technologically advanced societies and brought with them primitive farming techniques. They lived a less nomadic life than the native hunter-gatherers and sowed small fields with cereals or pulses to supplement their diet. The Celtic people were highly religious and ritually buried their dead. If the deceased was of high status, valuable artefacts such as flint tools, arrow heads, wild boar tusks and sections of antlers were buried with the body.

Later immigrants brought ever more sophisticated farming practices involving the use of ploughs, draught animals and livestock. Increasingly large fields were created by clearing more of the woodland with fire and axe, and, by 1200BC, agriculture had transformed the landscape. Farmed land had been separated by mud banks into individual fields and ploughs were drawn by oxen. The staple crops were barley, oats, rye and wheat. Cattle, sheep and pigs were the main livestock. Domestic pigs had to be nightly herded back into enclosures to prevent male wild boar mating with the domestic sows and attacking the domestic boars. Wild boar are the ancestors of all domestic pigs and early domestic breeds were more like small wild boar than the large multi-coloured varieties seen today. Interbreeding between wild boar and domesticated pigs was a common occurrence. Ripening crops also had to be protected from foraging wild animals at night, particularly wild boar. This incompatibility with farming practices, combined with the continual loss of their woodland habitat, meant the writing was on the wall for the wild boar of Britain.

The Celts

The Celtic people of Britain lived as tribal societies. Their culture continued to grow and by the last millennium BC they lived in wooden huts with thatched roofs and clay plastered walls. Leather sandals or shoes were worn and their clothes were dyed bright colours. They made their own utensils, jewellery and ornaments using tin from Cornwall, iron from Sussex and copper from south west Ireland, traded for hides, livestock and slaves. Gold and silver were traded from abroad. Celtic artefacts, and later coinage, often depict-ed wild animals important to their culture. Wild boar featured prominently in this iconography, their image representing strength, bravery and ferocity. In Celtic mythology the goddess of the forest and hunting, Ardwinna, was often depicted riding on the back of a wild boar.

Ardwinna, riding a boar.

When hunted, an irate or exhausted wild boar will stand its ground and charge its attackers. This fierce self-defence and the difficulty of killing an animal (due to its tough hide) led to its symbolic association with battle and conquest. Celtic war standards and helmets often depicted wild boar. The mouth of a Celtic war trumpet, an instrument used to intimidate an enemy with blaring sound, was frequently in the shape of a wild boar. To the Celtic tribes of Britain, wild boar became a religious icon as well as a provider of food.

Celtic culture was widespread in Britain when the first Roman army, under Julius Caesar, invaded in 54BC. The Romans were already familiar with the symbolic importance of wild boar. For example the 20th legion, which was part of the massive army sent by Emperor Claudius in AD43 to occupy Britain, had adopted a running wild boar as its emblem. The 20th legion later played a leading role in the defeat, in Warwickshire, England, of the rebellious Celtic queen Boadicea, leader of the Iceni tribe.

The Dark Ages followed the Romans' withdrawal around AD410. A defensively vulnerable Britain was invaded by waves of Germanic tribes of Angles, Saxons and Jutes. The immigrants arrived in a combination of peaceful settlement and violent conquest. The English and Germanic tribes often intermixed or coexisted but the Scots, Welsh, Irish and Cornish kept the Anglo-Saxons at bay and formed the 'Celtic fringe' surrounding England.

Myths and legends

Celtic mythology involving wild boar typically had associations with death, destruction and the underworld. The wild boars' feisty nature, their habit of digging up the earth for food and nocturnal wanderings suggested these dark associations.

Around AD500 stories circulated about a man called Arthur who routed an Anglo-Saxon army at the Battle of Mount Badon. In later writings fact mixed with fiction and 'King' Arthur became immortalised as Britain's legendary defender against the marauding Saxons.

King Arthur had his own mythical run-in with a wild boar. In one Arthurian legend, the tale of Culhwch and Olwen, Arthur had to hunt a wild boar known as Twrch Trwyth. The story illustrates well the dark and destructive images associated with wild boar. The hero Culhwch was to marry Olwen, daughter of the uncouth giant Ysbaddaden. Ysbaddaden was not keen on the wedding and to prevent it ordered Culhwch to first accomplish several near impossible tasks. One task was to acquire from the wild boar Twrch Trwyth a razor, scissors and comb. These grooming implements were needed to tidy up the appearance of Ysbaddaden for the big day. Only the razor, scissors and comb used by the wild boar would be strong enough to cope with the giant's unruly hair and beard. Twrch Trwyth was originally a King but had been transformed into a wild boar by God as punishment for his wickedness. He was so dangerous that Culhwch was not expected to survive the hunt so Culhwch went to his first-cousin, King Arthur, for help.

The fearsome wild boar was known to be in Ireland where it had already laid waste to a third of the country's land. One of Arthur's men, disguised as a bird, failed in an audacious attempt to snatch the comb and scissors from between the ears of the boar. A final plea by Arthur to give up the wedding items was refused as Twrch Trwyth would rather die than surrender. Twrch Trwyth was accompanied by seven young wild boar so Arthur assembled a large hunting party of many men and dogs. The boar were hunted from Ireland to Wales then Brittany and finally Cornwall. The hunt raged for eleven days and dozens of Arthur's men died in the struggle as did the seven wild boar that accompanied Twrch Trwyth. Finally the great boar was driven into the River Severn. The water temporarily overwhelmed him and the razor and scissors were plucked from between his ears. Twrch Trwyth recovered his balance but was driven further out and into the sea where the comb was eventually taken from him. The final fate of Twrch Trwyth and the hounds that followed him was unknown. The tale had a happy ending as grooming the unkempt Ysbaddaden proved fatal to the giant and the lovers Culhwch and Olwen could marry in peace.

The coat of arms granted to Ammanford District Council, Carmarthenshire, Wales, in 1952 depicts a wild boar in recognition of King Arthur hunting the wild boar, Twrch Trwyth, in the Amman Valley.

The coming of Christianity

The new Christian religion became more readily accepted in Britain around AD600 when the Saxon king, Ethelbert of Kent, converted to Christianity. Many of the native Celtic population had already converted to Christianity, but the incoming Saxons were pagan. Pagan festivals and myths began to be adapted and incorporated into Christian myth-ology to draw people gradually into the new faith. The Christian religions' Easter period of Lent provides an example. 'Easter' itself is an Anglo-Saxon word derived from the name of the Anglo-Saxon goddess of spring, 'Eastre' or 'Eostre'. The word 'Lent' is derived from the old Anglo-Saxon word 'lencten', meaning 'spring'.

Spring is the season of new life and revival from the cold dark winter and was universally celebrated by pagan cultures. Rituals typically re-enacted ancient regeneration myths to encourage crops to grow and livestock to reproduce after winter dormancy. Myths often exist in several versions but with a common theme; in the case of spring the theme is death and resurrection. Wild boar, perhaps not surprisingly when death and darkness are the theme, had a role to play in these resurrection myths. The myths concerning the origin of Easter centred on the fertility god, Tammuz, who was a shepherd gored to death by a wild boar while tending his flock. The mourning over his death continued for 40 days and nights to commemorate the 40 years of Tammuz's life. The myth records that Tammuz's distraught wife, the goddess of nature Ishtar, followed him into the underworld causing the onset of winter to the earth above. To restore life to the land, Tammuz was resurrected every spring and followed out of the underworld by his wife, allowing six months of sunlight to return to the land enabling the crops to grow. He must then return to the underworld, again pursued by his grieving wife, causing the onset of another winter. Ham traditionally eaten on Easter Sunday is symbolic revenge against the wild boar that killed Tammuz. Lent was originally a pagan celebration of fasting and mourning over the death of Tammuz. The Christian religion later adapted the Easter period to commemorate Christ's resurrection. The meaning of the 40 days of fasting and penitence was changed to recognition of Christ's fasting in the wilderness.

In the 9th century, Britain was invaded by the Norsemen. Due to their refusal to embrace the new Christian religion these Norwegian Vikings and Danes were referred to at the time as the 'great heathen host'. In AD871 King Athelred I (reigned 865-871) and his brother Alfred led the Saxon army at Ashdown, Reading, to victory against the invading Norse. Alfred, in the words of Anglo-Saxon chroniclers, had charged at the enemy, 'like a wild boar'. A few years later Alfred, now King Alfred of Wessex (reigned 871-899), was attacked by the Norse under cover of a truce and fled from Wiltshire to the Somerset marshes. Sheltering in a swineherd's hut, he famously 'burnt the cakes' and was scolded furiously by the host's wife. A Viking force, under the leadership of Olaf Tryggvason of Norway and King Svein of Denmark, returned in 994 and attacked London and the south coast in an orgy of looting, burning and killing. To illustrate Olaf's strength in battle, a drawing in the margins of a Norse book depicts Olaf, sword in hand, in close combat with a wild boar.

The Middle Ages

The last Anglo-Saxon king, Harold II, and Britain's remnant Celtic culture were destroyed with the arrival of the Normans in 1066. However, the country's wild boar population was allowed a stay of execution because William 'the Conqueror' (reigned 1066-1087) was passionate about hunting. William set aside large tracts of land for the sole purpose of protecting and preserving game animals such as wild boar and deer for the Royal hunt. The New Forest in Hampshire was the first of many such Royal forests created on his orders in 1078 as a Royal Hunting Preserve. The king hunted for sport but most hunting was carried out by specially appointed professionals to provide meat for feasts and gifts.

'Crown-rights' over Royal forests were ruthlessly exercised and the 'forest-laws' that enforced them were hated by the local populace. Villages in areas decreed to be a Royal Forest had even been destroyed and the residents evicted. Forest-laws outlawed the use by the local peasantry of the wood-lands' natural resources such as timber and game animals. Hunting even small game such as rabbits and hares was strictly prohibited. No weapons were allowed to be carried in the forest and travellers had to keep to the highways running through the woods. These were desperate times for the poor and needy and this was the era that spawned the stories of Robin Hood and his band of merry men. These forest-dwelling outlaws held up the carriages travelling along the woodland roads 'robbing from the rich to give to the poor'.

Forest laws were administered by an army of staff and the more serious offences were often heard in a travelling court called an 'eyre'. 'Swainmote' is an Old English term meaning 'a meeting of swineherds' and the 'swainmote' was a court held several times a year to control the pannaging of domestic pigs in the forest. One original medieval title is still in use today: in the New Forest 'verderers' remain the judicial officers administering to the forest.

In 1087, William conducted a survey of his English lands and recorded the results in the Domesday Book. He found the primeval wildwood virtually all gone and woodland and wood pasture covered only 15% of the land. The king himself was gone the same year, dying from internal injuries following a riding accident whilst hunting the French at a garrison in Mantes. Misfortune befell the family on two other occasions: William's second son, Richard, had died several years earlier from a riding accident when hunting, and in 1100, William's son and successor, King William Rufus II (reigned 1087 –1100), was accidentally shot dead by an arrow allegedly from the French knight, Sir Walter Tirel, Lord of Poix, whilst hunting in the New Forest. The king was nicknamed 'Rufus' because of his choleric red complexion, no doubt the same colour of the French knight as he immediately fled back to his homeland. However, suspicion still remains that it may not have been an accident. Prince Henry, Rufus's younger brother, who was part of the hunting party, immediately rode to the royal treasury at Winchester where, three days later, he was crowned king. His older brother, Robert Duke of Normandy, was conveniently away at the Crusades at the time.

King Henry I (reigned 1100-1135) and later King Henry II (reigned 1154-1189) further expanded the range of Royal Forests in England. In medieval times the word 'forest' did not necessarily imply just woodland, as it does today. Heathland, moorland and even agricultural land could all be designated as 'forest' and was done so to provide the diversity of habitat and access to agricultural crops that wild boar and deer thrive on. By Henry II's reign, one-third of the entire English Kingdom consisted of land designated as Royal Forests. The situation had become intolerable for the peasants evicted from their homes and land, and denied the freedom to make a living from the forest. However, only when the country's barons and noble men began to suffer financial hardship from lost crop land and increased taxation did a revolt begin. The outcome was that in 1215 the Magna Carta was signed at Runnymede, Surrey, whereby the Plantagenet king, John (reigned 1199-1216), reluctantly curbed the excessive political power of the ruling Royal family. The forest laws were reformed and barbaric punishments of amputation or death for poaching animals, such as wild boar and deer from the Royal Forests, were outlawed.

Wild boar have another trait, aside from being a popular quarry species, that helped seal their fate: their meat is of excellent flavour. It was traditionally served at ritualistic feasts throughout the ages; it was the unsustainable decadence of the medieval royals that proved too much for the remaining wild boar. The dinner bell became their death knell. It was recorded that Henry III (reigned 1216-1272), for Christmas dinner in 1251, had 200 wild boar delivered from the Forest of Dean in Gloucestershire and 100 from Pickering forest in Yorkshire. They were no doubt ordered for a feast of celebration because on Boxing Day Henry III's daughter, Margaret, married the Scottish king, Alexander III, in York Abbey. The newly-weds were unlikely to have had large appetites, Margaret was only 11 years old and Alexander just 10. It is not difficult to picture the medieval banquet where wild boar would be served. Long wooden tables lit by candles in a great beamed hall would be strewn with a variety of meats washed down with flagons of mead or wine. The wild boar's head would be ceremoniously carried to the high table by the *sewer,* the medieval equivalent of today's *maître d'*.

Henry III died in old age, rather than from a surfeit of wild boar meat, and was succeeded by his son, Edward I (reigned 1272-1307). In 1282 a record from an eyre court shows four wild boars and three sows were taken without Royal Warrant from the Forest of Dean by Edward I's brother, Edmund. An undated record shows a request for an unknown number of wild boar from the Forest of Dean, for Edward II (reigned 1307-1327), could not be fulfilled. Wild boar therefore may have become extinct from one of their last protected strongholds, the Forest of Dean, around the turn of the 14th century.

Royal associations with wild boar continued despite their absence from most, if not all, of Britain. The use of the animal as a symbol of status, wealth and power increased with the new fashion for heraldic devices. The use of a heraldic Coat

The coat of arms of Hinckley and Bosworth district council. 'Post proelia concordia' *means 'After conflict, peace.'*

of Arms to display a nobleman's aristocratic lineage became popular in the 13th and 14th centuries. Because of their fierce reputation, wild boar were regularly depicted on a Coat of Arms to symbolise a brave warrior. Heraldic terms were derived mainly from Norman-French language of the time. Wild boar were typically pictured as *passant* (walking with three feet on the ground and the right fore-foot raised), *statant* (standing still with all four feet on the ground) or *enraged* (standing on hind legs with fore-legs raised). Different parts of the animals' anatomy could be: *armed* (tusks are coloured differently from the rest of the animal), *crined* (mane is coloured differently), *unguled* (hoofs are a different colour), *cleyed* (depicted with claws) or *membered* (tongue visible). Richard III (reigned 1483-1485) of the House of York, when he was Duke of Gloucester, adopted a white wild boar as his emblem. Richard was defeated by Henry VII (reigned 1485-1509) at the Battle of Bosworth in Leicestershire, the last of the Wars of the Roses, and the Tudor dynasty was established. Today, the coat of arms of Bosworth District Council recalls the battle and features the passant white boar of Richard III being attacked by the red dragon emblem of Henry VII. It was rumoured that many innkeepers of the time hastily painted over the white boar emblem of the defeated Richard in a less contentious colour.

Tales of derring-do

There are many tales of heroic courage that have a ferocious wild boar as the main adversary. One tale, set some 500 years ago in Cliffe Wood, Bradford, has deceit as the theme. It tells of a ferocious boar that lived in the woods on the outskirts of the town. The boar terrorised the local people and damaged so much land and property that the government offered a reward for anyone brave enough to slay the beast.

The coat of arms for Bradford City Council showing a wild boar's head with missing tongue.

On St Martin's Day the King would present the reward to whoever delivered the beast. A crafty woodsman took up the King's offer and hid in an oak tree in an area of the wood where the boar frequently drank, known as Boars' Well. He waited patiently, ready to slay his quarry and claim the reward. The boar duly arrived and was shot by an arrow from the woodsman's bow. The boar's carcass was too heavy to move so the woodsman cut out the boar's tongue as proof of his victory and returned to the town. A short time later, another hunter who had heard of the King's offer, was passing through the woods and saw the slain boar lying near the well and had the idea of claiming the reward. Again the boar was too heavy to move, so he cut off the boar's head and left for the town. Arriving before the true victor, he was presented to the King to claim his reward. The King inspected the boar's head but when asked, the man could offer no suitable explanation as to why the tongue was missing. The first hunter then arrived, explained the true circumstances of the defeat and showed the boar's tongue as evidence. He received his rightful reward: a plot of land called Hunt Yard in Great Horton, just outside the town. The coat of arms for Bradford City Council depicts a boar's head missing a tongue. Part of Bradford District is still referred to as Boar's Well, and rather fittingly, part of it is now a Nature Reserve.

A local legend describes how Sutton Coldfield in Warwickshire became a Royal town. The tale recounts how Henry VIII (reigned 1509-1547) was out hunting in Sutton Park, Warwickshire, with his friend Bishop Vesey when he was unexpectedly charged by an enraged wild boar. Before the animal could harm the King, it was killed by an arrow through the heart. Henry called for the unseen marksman to be brought to him so he could express his gratitude and was surprised when a beautiful young woman came forward. To reward her, the king restored property to her family of which they had previously been dispossessed. The King also presented her with the Tudor Rose, his family emblem, which could now be used also as the emblem of Sutton Coldfield, the girl's native town. To the people of Sutton a Royal Charter was signed in 1528 giving Sutton Coldfield the title of Royal Town and Sutton Park to the people of Sutton in perpetuity.

The theme of saving the King through a feat of strength or bravery is common in wild boar legends, particularly those involving Scottish clans. For example, a *passant* wild boar with an arrow through its side is found on the crest of Clan Pollock. Around AD1200 the chief of the Pollock clan saved the King from an attacking wild boar whilst out hunting in a Royal forest. The King knighted the Pollock chief for his bold and timely assistance. Similarly, the MacGregor clans' coat of arms displays a sword with a crown on its point

The badge of the Clan MacKinnon. 'Audentes Fortuna Juvat' means 'Fortune Assists the Daring'.

crossed with an oak tree. The legend tells that Malcolm MacGregor saved King Malcolm IV of Scotland's (reigned 1153-1165) life whilst out hunting. The King was unmounted when a wild boar charged him. Malcolm MacGregor uprooted a small oak tree which he used to hold the boar at bay until he was able to draw his sword and slay the beast. In gratitude the King conferred on him the coat of arms displaying the crown, sword and oak tree. An ancestor of the Clan Baird is also reputed to have saved the Scottish King William the Lion (reigned 1165-1214) from an aggressive wild boar and was rewarded with lands in Lanarkshire. Similar stories are also attributed to the Clans Chisolm, Baird and Campbell.

The Clan MacKinnon crest pictures a wild boar's head, but unusually there is the shank-bone of a deer in its mouth. The story was that a MacKinnon was hunting on the shores of Loch Scavaig in Skye when he became separated from his colleagues. Sheltering in a cave for the night he lit a fire to roast some venison. A wild boar then entered the cave and attacked him as he was carving the meat. He thrust the meat into the boar's mouth to jam it open before killing the animal with his knife.

Ramming an object into the snaggle-toothed mouth of an attacking wild boar, usually whatever is carried in the hand at the time, is another common theme in wild boar legends. According to tradition, in the time of James II of Scotland (reigned 1437-1460), Duncan Campbell of Lochow was living in a cave near Loch Lomond with a lady with whom he had eloped. Near to the cave lived a typically ferocious wild boar that much troubled the local people. Duncan threw a stone into the beast's mouth and then dispatched it with his dirk (a long dagger carried by the Highlanders). The King pardoned Campbell who was able to return home with his lady friend.

In 14th Century England, an Oxford University student was reputedly out walking on Christmas Day in local woodland. He was reading Aristotle when suddenly a wild boar attacked him. At the last moment the student managed to ram the book down the animal's throat and the boar choked to death. The student cut off the animal's head and returned to college with it so he could retrieve his book. To this day, the incident is still celebrated annually at Queens College, Oxford. In the ceremony of the Boars' Head, a wild boar's head decorated with rosemary, bay and holly, and with an orange in its mouth, is served to the assembled guests.

Final demise and re-introduction attempts

During Elizabeth I's reign (1558-1603), even more woodland habitat was destroyed to fuel the charcoal burning furnaces, known as bloomeries, in which iron-ore was smelted. Wild boar hunting had now ceased as a Royal sport because the quarry was all but extinct. Domestic pigs were increasingly being run through the forests during the autumn to fatten up on the falling acorns. Autumn is also the rutting season for wild boar and the final few wild boar were absorbed into pannaged domestic herds and lost as a separate species. The date at which wild boar finally became extinct in Britain is unclear due to subsequent attempts by landed gentry to re-introduce animals from the Continent. It is generally believed that free-living wild boar became extinct in England at the turn of the 14th century and during the 16th century in Scotland.

However, there are references to wild boar in England later than the 14th century. For example, there are records of wild boar in Savernake Forest, Wiltshire, in 1539 and 1543 and Chartley Park, Stafford, in 1593 and 1683. It is thought that these records refer to animals introduced from the Continent into managed hunting estates as status symbols for landed gentry. Similarly, Sutton Park, in Sutton Coldfield, Warwickshire, may have had wild boar present there during the reign of Henry VIII. King James VI of Scotland (reigned 1567-1625), who on the death of Elizabeth also became James I of England (reigned 1603-1625), must have regretted the passing of the boar hunt and the loss of a status symbol. Whilst attempting to cement relations between the English and Scottish parliaments and counting his blessing over the failed Gunpowder plot, he imported wild boar from France and released them into Windsor Park in 1608 and again in 1611. James I may have been the 'wisest fool in Christendom', but his attempts at re-introducing the wild boar were initially successful because there are records of wild boar in Windsor Park in 1617. The eventual fate of the animals is unrecorded. The following king, Charles I (reigned 1625-1649), also had a passion for boar hunting and, like his father before him, tried to re-introduce wild boar by releasing animals imported from Germany into the New Forest in Hampshire.

The popularity of wild boar with Royalty was not shared by the local populace. According to the diarist John Aubrey, the wild boar Charles released into the New Forest 'increased and became terrible to the travellers. In the civil warres they were destroyed but they had tainted all the breeds of pigges in the neighbouring partes, which are of their colour; a kind of soot colour.' The last sentence exemplifies the unfortunate willingness of wild boar to out-breed with domestic stock. The New Forest wild boar did not survive the animosity of the local farmers but Charles had bigger worries: war with Spain (again), war with France and civil war within. Charles lost his civil war and his head, for treason, in 1649 outside the Banqueting Hall in Whitehall.

A further re-introduction of wild boar, which was equally unpopular, was documented for the late 17thC. The grandly titled General Emanuel Scroope Howe, according to a letter written by The Reverend Gilbert White (the vicar of Selborne who devoted his life to observing plant, animal and bird life), turned some wild boar from Germany out into the forests of Alice Holt in Surrey. Again unpopular with the locals, they were not allowed to live long.

Towards the end of the 17th century all the wild boar in Britain, original or introduced, had died out. Habitat loss, over-hunting and finally absorption into the herds of domestic pigs that were pannaged in the woods, ended their reign. The wild boar, a species that had played such a prominent role in British history, culture and heritage, was now extinct.

And so it remained, until now.

2

THEIR RETURN

Farming

In the late 1970s and early 80s cheaper travel costs allowed more and more British people to holiday in Continental Europe. The cuisines of different cultures were sampled and many tourists experienced for the first time the taste of wild boar meat. They found it to their liking. A few enterprising British farmers began to breed the animals to supply the new and growing home market for wild boar products. The meat was promoted as 'one of the finest game meats; the colour of venison, the texture of best beef, and without any pork flavour'. Wild boar have a higher ratio of red muscle fibres to white than domestic pigs, thus the meat is dark red in appearance. The flavour is subtle and gamey with no suggestion of a pork taste. It is low in cholesterol and seen as clean and healthy. It is not at all like pork in flavour, texture or colour.

Husbanded wild boar are genetically the same as free-living wild boar and farming was based on controlling a wild animal rather than domestication - a method that allowed the stock to live in accordance with their own natural seasons of growth and breeding. Unforced growth rates and a predominantly natural diet ensured less carcass fat than was found on their domestic counterparts. In the kitchen, the undesirable and off-putting watery blobs of white fatty deposits seen when intensively reared pork is cooked, a condition known as PSE (pale, soft and exudative), did not occur with cuts of wild boar meat. Benefits to the farmer, compared to rearing domestic pigs, were that the animals remained hardy and rarely affected by disease. Also no farrowing assistance was ever required, not that it would have been allowed by the sows, who are notoriously bad tempered at this time.

The first wild boar farm began in Cambridgeshire in 1981 using surplus animals from London Zoo, descendants of stock originally imported from France. In 1988 there were 3 licensed breeders with a total of 38 animals between them. This had grown to 18 breeders in 1989 and by 1994 there were estimated to be around 40 farms commercially breeding wild boar with some 400 sows producing about 1,500 animals a year for slaughter. The figures are only estimates because no central register of wild boar farm stock has ever been compiled. The Government department overseeing agricultural interests does not differentiate wild boar stock from domestic pig stock. Wild boar farming had grown quicker than the legislation policing it. A more accurate estimate of numbers was recorded for the year 2000. A survey conducted by the Department for the Environment, Food and Rural Affairs (DEFRA) reported the much higher number of 4,554 wild boar now farmed in Britain.

In the late 1980s several farmers supplemented their original stock with animals of both west European and East European origin. The west European animals were of German origin and were imported from an estate in Denmark. The East European animals were imported from farm stock in Sweden. Both these countries have a similar high health status for pigs as Britain, allowing importation. East European wild boar were particularly sought after as they are a larger size than their west European counterparts. Incorporating East

European animals into a bloodline made economic sense as carcass weight was increased.

The number of wild boar farmers in Britain continued to increase but there was a change in farming methods. Breeding male wild boars had initially been confined to secure pens and the sows housed in larger straw covered pens or small paddocks. However, to obtain a better flavoured product and compete with the market for imported Continental wild boar meat, wild boar in Britain began to be kept in more extensive conditions. Farming practices changed to mimic those practised in France where the wild boar have access to woodland. In this environment the animals can forage for a diverse array of natural foods, benefiting from a more natural diet and less stressful housing. These conditions produced optimum flavoured meat. However, when the wild boar in Britain began to be kept in these extensive conditions, the fun really began.

Escapology

Wild boar are the Houdinis of captive livestock. They have the build for it. A strong narrow snout on a large head supported by powerful shoulders is the ideal tool for undermining and levering up stock fencing. Long legs provide a quick turn of speed and their jumping ability is more akin to a deer than a pig. Stories of escaped wild boar were reported quite regularly in the press. Between 1983 and 1994 over 60 wild boar from 6 different farms in 6 different counties were recorded as having escaped from farm establishments.

In south west Kent, the great storm of 1987 blew down a section of perimeter fencing on a wild boar farm in Tenterden. Several wild boar were rumoured to have immediately uppedsticks and left for pastures new although the owners repeatedly denied losing any stock. Escaping farm stock is the ideal seed to start a new population as the escapees are likely to already be in family groups. The naturally secretive and nocturnal behaviour of the newly liberated animals meant they were seldom seen. Early sightings in Tenterden and neighbouring districts were treated with disbelief, suspicion or as a case of mistaken identity. For example, there was a newspaper article the local *Kentish Express* in 1991. An eyewitness reported the sighting of an animal crossing a road at night, close to the Tenterden wild boar farm, that had the appearance of a small bear. A juvenile wild boar trotting over the ground actually looks remarkably like a small bear on all fours: all shaggy brown fur and bobbing rump as it kicks its back legs out. The described height, length and coat colour all matched that of a young wild boar. The article referred to a similar report from a car driver in the same area three years earlier. With hindsight the mystery animals were most probably wild boar although the suggestion at the time was of a large badger. The lady reporting the incident was unimpressed with the badger explanation.

The badger has covered for the wild boar in another way. Rooted patches of bare earth in pasture fields where the grass had been torn up were initially attributed to badgers, which are well known to search for worms and grubs in this manner. Wild boar also root up pasture during their nocturnal feeds but tell-tale evidence of the wild boars' cleft hoof prints were lost amongst a myriad of clefted sheep or cattle prints. It wasn't until 1994 that the animals' presence was verified beyond doubt when local huntsmen in the neighbouring parish of Beckley, just across the Kent border inside East Sussex, shot two wild boar that were rooting up farmland. A carcass was hard evidence to discredit. Compulsory identity tagging of farmed wild boar is not required by law so the owner of the escaped animals could not be traced. Identity tagging a wild boar's ear is not an easy process. The animals greatly resent being restrained and can become highly excitable and uncontrollable. However, the two animals shot rooting up farmland in Beckley had probably been born in the wild and were descendants of the original founding fathers. They would not have identity tags even if their parents did.

Two years later, in 1996, there was further evidence of the presence of free-living wild boar when damage to a maize crop was reported by a perplexed farmer in the parish of Aldington, some 12.5 miles away in south west Kent. The damage was attributed to wild boar when several were shot in adjacent woodland. These animals were reported to originate from a different source, escapees from an abattoir in Ashford, Kent, a few years earlier.

Official recognition

Unable to ignore the clamour from the farming community in the areas where the boar were alleged to live, the then Ministry of Agriculture, Fisheries and Food began in 1996 an enquiry into the free-living wild boar. This incidentally is where my involvement with the wild boar began. I was given the task of verifying which localities, initially in southern England, contained evidence of wild boar.

I ensconced myself in a very welcoming and atmospheric farmhouse bed and breakfast on the Kent/ East Sussex border. The kitchen had rows of hop flowers running along the tops of cupboards and from the ceiling hung racks strewn with implements used for farming sheep in a previous era. Devices for shearing, injecting or castrating resembled medieval torture implements rather than farming bygones. Antique cuckoo clocks hung on every wall and each clock ticked or squawked a different time, but if an average was taken, a surprisingly reliable estimate of the time was achieved.

My first port of call was the forthright wife of a gentleman farmer whose hop garden, after a visit from a group of wild boar, resembled a battlefield at the Somme.

After I had introduced myself, a plummy voice demanded, 'Why have you got the job?'

Taken aback, I replied, 'Proven ability.'

I had just returned from a month's fieldwork in the Outer Hebrides where I studied rat predation on nesting seabirds. The only thing I had proved was that I could survive on a rocky island without being blown off the cliff. The real reason I was in the job because I was at the right place at the right time. But that was not what she wanted to hear.

I won my acceptance when a particularly irascible and uncommunicative farmer, all red faced from shattered veins and exertion, asked me to help him lift a load of manure onto the top of an enormous dung heap. For some reason it had to be put on the top, the side wouldn't do. I did not bat an eyelid and climbed up with him, my wellies filling with straw and muck as I went. I was on all fours at one stage after slipping for the umpteenth time. I was plastered in the foul smelling stuff. The task done, he happily chatted away about the wild boar that had been foraging on his land.

Several months later, when the dogs at the B&B had stopped barking at my coming and going and the cuckooing clocks no longer kept me awake at night, I had confirmed that wild boar existed in woodlands in many areas of Kent and East Sussex. In fact, field signs of wild boar were found in an area of approximately 67.5 sq. miles. I also found evidence of wild boar across the south coast in several parishes in Dorset. The free-living wild boar in Dorset were alleged to have originated from a mass break-out from a now defunct wild boar farm in the parish of Bridport.

A free-living wild boar in East Sussex emerges from the undergrowth in fading evening light.

Free-living wild boar had, for the first time in at least 300 years, returned to Britain.

The flood gates open

Since 2003 the trickle of escapees dripping into the countryside has become a flood. The deliberate release of farmed boar by individuals opposed on moral grounds to the farming of animals for meat, combined with deliberate releases by those impatient to see wild boar back in Britain in greater numbers than at present, has resulted in wild boar inhabiting many more counties in Britain. Aside from Dorset, East Sussex and Kent, breeding populations of wild boar are now established in Cornwall, Devon, Gloucestershire, Herefordshire, West Sussex, Warwickshire and Yorkshire. Furthermore, the boar have now crossed national boundaries as the Gloucestershire 'Forest of Dean' boar have forded the River Wye into Monmouthshire,

Wales, and a small isolated population has been recorded north of Fort William in the Scottish Highlands. It is quite obvious that as long as wild boar are kept in captivity in Britain, there will be further instances of escapes.

It is perfectly feasible for new populations to establish from escaped stock in many other areas of Britain. Firstly, luck plays an important role. To escape into a rural area, rich in woodland and low in human population, as the Kent/East Sussex escapees originally did, was fortunate. By contrast, an escaped wild boar that found itself in a housing estate in Gateshead, Tyneside, was not so lucky and was shot dead by police marksmen as it 'was posing a danger to the public as it was becoming more agitated'. Similarly, an escaped wild boar in Penzance, in a highly excitable state, was reportedly shot trying to enter a house by jumping through a window.

The failure of a farmer to quickly notify the relevant authorities of escaped animals allows time for the escapee(s) to disperse. If the escape is not noticed or reported at all, there would be no attempt to recapture or dispatch the errant beast(s). They would have ample time to travel many miles from the point of escape looking for suitable habitat. Wild boar can travel over 10 miles in a single night although about a mile is the norm. Multiple escapes would have the best chance of establishing a free-living population, and breached fencing, caused by a fallen tree for example, would provide such an opportunity. Animals escaping from establishments where they had access to woodland would be more used to foraging for natural seasonal foods and would possibly be better prepared for a life of unexpected freedom. Wild boar in captivity are more active during daylight than their wild counterparts but, once liberated, escapees soon revert to type, particularly if lead shot from a gun is fizzing past their ears.

In many privately owned woodlands, once the free-living

wild boars' presence was proven beyond doubt, a veil of secrecy was often drawn around which woodlands contained them so as to safeguard local shooting interests. Wild boar on the Continent are one of the most prestigious and popular animals to hunt and high prices are paid for the privilege. Members of the hunting fraternity in several areas in Britain found this sport on their doorstep for free and woodlands containing wild boar became jealously guarded. Carcasses from hunted animals were sold to local game-dealers for sufficient sums of money to enable several hunters to upgrade their firepower and add telescopic sights with night vision capability. Local pubs and restaurants began to serve wild boar meat and the species acquired an economic value. It became in the hunters' interest to harvest rather than eradicate. A self-imposed cease-fire was even put in place on certain farmlands during the spring farrowing period when sows had dependent young.

This was not so much a display of humanity but rather to safeguard next year's crop of animals. Early attempts by farmers (unsympathetic to the wild boar's presence) to control the increasing wild boar population by trapping and shooting were ineffective. A lack of co-operation from neighbouring farmers sympathetic to the animals' presence enabled these wild-boar-friendly estates to act as safe refuge areas. In such areas the animals could breed undisturbed and re-colonise areas previously cleansed of wild boar.

The wild boar in Kent and East Sussex, for example, were also fortunate to have a wildlife corridor of thorny scrubland beneath high voltage power cables running inland from Dungeness Power Station. Wild boar travelling their nightly feeding routes are reluctant to move over open ground for fear of attack, preferring to use cover from hedgerows, tree lines and wood perimeters. This linear corridor runs for several miles through woodland and farmland allowing the wild boar secret passage to and from distant feeding areas. Dispersal into new territories was also aided, allowing the population contact with other unrelated wild boar. Similarly, the Dorset boar had a large acreage of agricultural land in which to go about their business unseen, and the boar in the vastness of the Forest of Dean were completely spoiled for the solitude and the rich pickings that such an area can provide. The remoteness of Exmoor was also the fillip the boar in North Devon needed to kick-start their successful re-introduction.

It can be speculated that the most likely reason why the majority of wild boar populations in Britain successfully established was the unreported multiple escapes of animals into sparsely populated agricultural or wooded countryside. Refuge areas allowed the populations to increase and man-made wildlife corridors, crop cover, or tree cover, allowed safe passage to and from feeding grounds and dispersal into new territories. Initial sightings and field signs were mistaken for other mammals and, once their presence was discovered, the wild boar were further protected by landowners who realised their sporting and economic value. Escapes from different sources provided the new genetic material needed to reduce the likelihood of inbreeding depression that would result in reduced litter sizes and weaker piglets.

There is no reason why this scenario cannot be repeated in other areas of Britain. Scotland, for example, has large tracts of forests compared to England and is ripe for re-colonisation; Wales too.

A successful species
Wild boar possess several characteristics that make them one of the earth's most successful mammal species. They

are adaptive to a wide range of geographical and climatic conditions, have a broad omnivorous diet, are prolific breeders and have multiple births. Also they are gregarious, aggressive when threatened and, most importantly, have an association with man (hunted and farmed). For a new mammal species to reach Britain, considerable stretches of water have to be crossed, and these will in most cases only be negotiable with the assistance of man. Consequently, human activity has played an important role in shaping the fauna of Britain: all mammal species naturalised in Britain since the last ice age have either been deliberately released, have accidentally escaped from captivity, or, as in the case of rats and mice, arrived as stowaways aboard shipping.

Wild boar have been eradicated from Britain before, so what is the prognosis for the new fledgeling populations? They have no natural predators and would undoubtedly spread if left to their own devices. Their destiny lies in the hand of man. In present day Britain, the Royal Family do not wield the same power as in previous ages and although the current heir to the throne will ride to the hounds and stalk the stag, he is also a conservationist. However, the management of the wild boar will be decided more on economic grounds than on their potential as a managed sporting quarry; wild boar can damage agricultural crops and harbour disease infectious to domestic livestock, thus rendering them an economic liability.

3

FIELD CRAFT

Field signs

For such large animals wild boar are remarkably elusive. Their daylight hours are spent lying hidden in dense vegetation, and they only emerge at dusk to begin their nightly foraging activities. How can you tell if these shy animals are in woodland in your neighbourhood? Fortunately their nocturnal behaviour leaves behind an array of field signs to betray their presence once daylight returns. Feeding, travelling, grooming and mating behaviour are all reflected in several characteristic field signs.

A severely rooted pasture field is the most obvious sign made by wild boar and was what first betrayed their return to Britain. When the pasture is wet from the first autumn rains, the wild boar venture into the fields rooting for worms and grubs. On rare occasions, much to the chagrin of the farmer, a field can be completely 'ploughed' by a group of wild boar in only one or two nights. More typically, the rooting occurs in only a few small patches. Badgers will also dig up pasture in search of food or to excavate latrines. However, wild boar rooting is characterised by small mats overturned turf at the edge of the rooted area. The absence of scratch marks from a badger's claws and the presence of wild boar prints should confirm the culprits to be wild boars. In softer substrate, for example the soil of a newly sown field, a rooting wild boar will often leave a narrow trail of

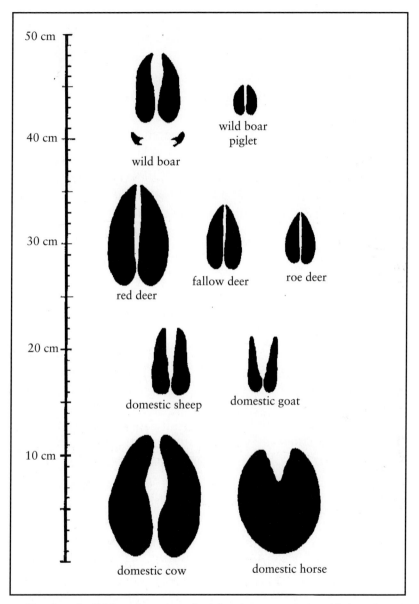

Tracks of wild boar compared with other mammals with hooves.

displaced earth several metres long. In these cases, the wild boar has walked forward without lifting its snout from the ground and ploughed a shallow furrow into the earth. The presence of prints in the soft ground again provide confirmation.

Wild boar prints can readily be distinguished from those of other ungulates because wild boar have large dew claws which are set low down and to the side of their limbs and are wider than the cleaves. In soft ground, a wild boar print can be distinguished from a deer print, for example, by the dew claws forming an impression outside the cleaves, even when the animal is walking only slowly. The prints will be of several different sizes when a group of the animals has been present. Piglet prints are tiny replicas of the adult's print but without an impression from the dew claws.

Signs of wild boar feeding within the woodland are most noticeable in late winter and spring when disturbance to the emerging vegetation is most pronounced. The leaf litter of deciduous woodland, as opposed to the carpet of needles in a coniferous woodland, is the wild boar's preferred rooting medium. Bracken, bluebells and wood anemones are often disturbed as the wild boar search for bulbs, roots and tender young shoots. The most important dietary items are the autumn fruits of acorns, chestnuts and beech mast that provide the females with the protein required for the forth-coming breeding season. Consequently, signs of rooting can be prevalent under fruit-bearing trees in the autumn.

To reach a feeding area wild boar will often travel the same route for several nights running. Feeding routes can be along hedgerows or tree lines, but existing tracks are also used, either made by man or another animal. Signs that prove wild boar are using a track can often be found: for example, hair snagged in a barbed wire fence as the animal dipped

Wild boar faecal pellets.

underneath. Wild boar have a thick bristly coat of brown hairs with white tips. When strands of the hair are caught in a wire, they have a similar appearance to the brindled hair of a badger. However, wild boar also possess an underlying pelage of lighter coloured fur which frequently is found snagged on the wire with the longer hairs. This tell-tale sign shows it was a wild boar passing through and not a badger. Further evidence can be provided by searching for prints either side of the fence and by the height of the wire: if it is 70cm above the ground, it is unlikely to be badger hair!

Faecal material is rarely found in feeding areas but can often be found along tracks leading to or from feeding routes. Defecating away from a feeding area is a deliberate policy to avoid betraying regularly used feeding areas to predators. Wild boar faecal pellets are larger and a different shape from other ruminant ungulates, consisting of irregularly shaped lumps up to 7cm thick and approximately 10cm long. They are black in colour but may possess a purplish hue when fresh. They turn grey after a time and break up into separate droppings.

Wild boar are able to penetrate wire stock fencing where

Characteristic arch left by wild boar in wire.

they leave a characteristically shaped arch to betray their presence. Unless being chased, a wild boar will not risk injury by bulldozing through an unbreached fence, but will make use of a weakness or gap in the fence made by, for example, the digging of a badger or rabbit. A wild boar's ability to jump over fencing is often understated. On more than one occasion a frightened animal has escaped from an abattoir by clearing a five bar gate in the manner of a champion hurdler.

Wild boar do not possess sweat glands and can suffer in hot weather. Wallowing in mud is the preferred method of keeping cool during the summer months. Wallows can readily be identified as an oval shaped impression in the mud; the sides of the impression are smooth where the animal has rolled. They occur anywhere an area of wet mud can be found and wild boar prints are usually in the immediate vicinity, if not in the wallow itself. Wallowing is frequently followed by an abrasive rub along a suitable 'rubbing tree' to aid removal of insects, parasites and moulting coat hair. Favoured trees can be rubbed to such an extent that bark is removed, the culprit identified by clumps of hair adhering to the sap that has oozed from the wounded tree. In exceptional cases the tree can become ring-barked. Occasionally a rubbing tree and wallow occur together.

Smaller trees are used in the wild boars' sexual behaviour of tusking, in which a notch of bark is removed from a young tree by the male's tusks, exposing the bare wood. Tusking posts can be found along the routes travelled by the male boars. They act as territorial signposts during the rut when the boars are sexually active. Pheromones in the boars' saliva leave a scent mark behind and a frequently notched tree has a distinct 'paisley' pattern scoured into the bark.

Sows farrow in the spring in specially constructed farrowing nests. Farrowing nests are well camouflaged as they are made from the surrounding vegetation. I once located a nest that a sow had recently vacated and went back the next day to show it to a colleague, but couldn't for the life of me find it again. First she digs a shallow hollow scrape in the ground and lines it with twigs and grasses. A mound of vegetation, for example bracken, reeds, twigs from the immediate area is piled on top of the scrape up to a metre in height. She enters into the mound and gives birth inside this protective covering. Wild boar sows are very protective mothers and, like most mammals, are more aggressive when accompanied by tiny offspring. It is therefore not sensible to search for farrowing nests to verify suspicions that wild boar are in a particular area.

Field signs are unstable and can quickly deteriorate in adverse weather. In particular, prints can become blurred around the edges in only a day or two, and distinguishing a wild boar print from that of other ungulates becomes difficult or impossible. Seasonality also affects field signs. Prints will not form in the hard dry ground in summer and rooting will only occur in a soft or damp substrate. Tusking trees only occurs during the autumn rut and the tree will seal its wounds the following spring and the notches become less visible.

One final note of caution. Domestic pigs have retained many of the behavioural traits of their wild boar ancestors and have a print that is identical. Bear this in mind before jumping to conclusions.

Watching wild boar

If you have noticed unusual field signs whilst out and about that have led you to believe there may be wild boar in your area, how can you be sure they belong to a wild boar and not an escaped domestic pig or species of deer? The answer is you cannot be certain without shooting, trapping or observing the animal(s) responsible. Shooting an animal solely to verify its identity is indefensibly immoral; we want to know what the animal *is*, rather than *was*. Trapping a potentially dangerous animal such as a wild boar should be left to experienced personnel. Observation is the correct method to use and, although observing wild boar is easier said than done, the odds can be weighted in your favour.

Contrary to their fierce reputation, wild boar will avoid human contact whenever possible. Their eyesight is poor and they can only recognise blue from the three primary colours. However, blue colours are most easily seen under poor light conditions, typically the time wild boar feed, so they are able to forage at night when their human adversaries would be floundering in the dark. If we should venture out after dark, good hearing and an exceptional sense of smell alert the wild boar to our presence long before we realise we are in their company. During the day, if aware of our scent, they will either stay motionless in their resting place until we have passed by or creep silently away. They will bolt only if we catch them unawares, usually when they are asleep or the direction of the wind has carried our scent away. When a disturbed wild boar bolts, there is a heart thumping explosion of bracken and bramble and a glimpse of brown rump crashing away through the undergrowth. Several times in the course of my work I have inadvertently flushed out a wild boar, and a minute or two later, a pheasant or woodcock has flown up from the ground in front of me. My heart, still pounding from the wild boar a few moments earlier, jumps violently again and I freeze; an involuntary reaction way out of proportion to a fleeing bird.

My first clear sighting of a free-living wild boar in Britain was by chance. A routine evening stroll was greatly enlivened by a male wild boar wandering out from the trees onto the grassy ride where I was walking. He scented the air against a background of oak and cherry and looked perfectly at home, as if his species had never been away. I felt I had been transported back in time and would not have been surprised to see a Royal hunting party come crashing round the corner. The boar became aware of me and quickly returned to cover, but I was fired to see more of these impressive and visually intimidating beasts.

My first deliberate attempt to view a wild boar was not a success. A local farmer offered to take me to an area where a wild boar often came to feed at night. We took up position and waited. It was a clear, cold night and although I was chilled to the bone I was determined not to retire to the warmth of the vehicle until the farmer suggested so. There was no way I was going to let him think I was 'soft'. Finally, close to my right I heard movement in the undergrowth and what I thought was the grunting of a wild boar. I nudged the farmer to draw his attention. He said nothing, which I took to mean shut up or you will frighten it away. I did not dare speak or move for the next 30 minutes.

No further noise was heard and nudging the farmer again I asked, 'What was that noise, it sounded like a wild boar?'

'What noise?' he replied with a start, 'I fell asleep an hour ago.'

I gave up there and then, thinking there must be an easier way than this.

My second attempt to see a free-living wild boar was equally unsuccessful. Shortly before nightfall the same farmer and I took up a standing position on a narrow woodland ride where wild boar prints had recently been found. I was to look for wild boar down the left of the ride and the farmer to the right. The moonlight would illuminate the ride sufficiently to allow us to identify a wild boar should one appear on the ride. Darkness fell and we soon heard the grunting of a wild boar, only the boar was not on the ride but in the pitch black of the woodland opposite our position. We remained in position and listened as the grunting and cracking of twigs told us the boar was heading in our direction. My excitement rose. The noise from snapping twigs and branches became increasingly loud and began to resemble an army tank crashing through the wood rather than an animal. The boar continued to work its way towards us and came so close I thought it was going to emerge from the trees directly in front of us, about two metres away. I realised this might not be good news, the boar would not be pleased to see us and startling it might cause it to react unpredictably. Just as the boar was about to come out from the trees I lost my nerve and coughed, loudly and deliberately. The boar realised he was not alone, barked an alarm and crashed back into the woods. I was immensely relieved and although eager to see a wild boar, I did not want it to be eyeball to eyeball. My companion must have also been relieved as he did not chastise me for sabotaging the event.

Armed with new advice from a wily old gamekeeper about how to safely watch wild boar, I employed different tactics which were considerably less nerve-racking and produced excellent results. I used bait stations. A bait station is an area within the wood where artificial feed is regularly placed to attract the target species to the area. Here is how it works.

Firstly, bait stations for wild boar should be established in areas where there are recent signs of feeding activity and little chance of disturbance from the general public. Needless to say, permission from the landowner must first be obtained. Watching wild boar takes time and effort that will be wasted if the landowner rumbles your little game. Whole maize is the preferred bait as it not affected by adverse weather conditions. The size of the grain is also large enough to deter the myriad of other woodland creatures and birds from devouring all the feed before the wild boar emerge. It is necessary to pre-bait for several days to accustom the suspicious wild boar to this unexpected manna-from-heaven. The bait should be spread about for maximum benefit because if the grain is placed in a single heap it will be dominated by one or two older animals who will drive other wild boar away, even if they belong to the same family group. Sub-dominant animals, juveniles and piglets will not get a look in and leave the station sooner than if the bait were scattered about.

When watching wary species such as wild boar, absolute silence, great patience and minimal personal scent will bring most reward. Wild boar have a very heightened sense of smell and hearing. It is not necessary to cover yourself in wild boar dung, but aftershave, perfume and fragrant soaps are not advisable. Nil by mouth is also a rule. Leave thermos flasks, sandwiches and wrapped toffees at home. To avoid disap-pointment, begin your observations only when the pre-bait is regularly taken. For a vantage point a high seat tied to a tree will prevent your scent from spooking the animals; alternatively, watch from inside a vehicle capable of negotiating the rough terrain of woodland rides. A distance of 30 metres from vantage point to bait is a good starting point, this can be steadily decreased as the wild boar become accustomed to feeding at the station.

Begin your observations approximately half an hour before sunset and continue after dark as a new bait station will only be visited after dark. Wild boar will become accustomed to a baited station that is continually in use and will visit it immediately they begin their nightly foraging. This is the ideal situation as there will still be sufficient daylight left to see the animals with the naked eye. Only once have I ever had a wild boar visit a bait station during the day: a sow and four piglets which were so small they must have only recently left the farrowing nest. The sow's need for nutrition overcame her natural reluctance to feeding in bright daylight. I sighted her by chance as I was only passing by the bait station - ample compensation for all previous vigils when no wild boar showed.

To clearly view wild boar feeding in the dark requires special night viewing equipment, a variety of which is readily available from shops catering for outdoor pursuits. My personal preference is a camcorder with night-sight capability (0 lux) used in conjunction with a powerful torch. The light beam from the torch, and this is the important bit, is covered by an infra-red filter (3mm semi-covert acrylic) which considerably enhances the night sight capability of the camcorder (and any other infra-red based night equipment). I prefer to use a camcorder so I can record my observations. They are light to hold and have excellent zoom capabilities allowing close-up observations. For the less financially challenged, night viewing binoculars that are a lot easier on the eyes than monocular equipment are available, but have the disadvantage that it is not possible to record your observations.

Bait stations should be discontinued when the ground becomes excessively rooted to allow the natural vegetation to regenerate. They can also attract the attention of poachers so use them wisely.

What you can expect to observe

Wild boar are the type of animal that make the hair on the back of your neck stand on end. Watching them feed at close quarters provides a heady mixture of apprehension and excitement enhanced by being deep in woodland, in fading light, in the presence of such a charismatic species. I have had on several occasions over two dozen wild boar at a bait station at any one time. Climbing down from a high seat in the dark to get back to my vehicle with wild boar scattering in every direction, barking and crashing through the undergrowth as they go, is guaranteed to get the heart racing.

The excitement of an evening's observation begins as soon as the animals can be heard moving in the distance. The light is usually beginning to fade and you listen intently for a confirmatory grunt or squeal. An impatience to view your quarry can make your imagination play tricks; a distant squeal may be a wild boar or the cry of a fox. A distant grunt or cough may be from a wild boar or domestic livestock in an adjacent field. The crack of twigs, becoming ever closer, gives the game away and signals the imminent arrival of the wild boar at the bait station.

At a newly established bait station, the wild boar will stop just short of the clearing where the bait is placed. They can be seen through the boughs of the trees standing motionless, scenting and listening for danger. At a bait station that has been in use for several weeks, the juvenile animals often rush straight onto the bait with no hesitation. Competition for the food overcomes the need to be wary. Often the wild boar have drying mud on their flanks from wallowing which gives them a piebald appearance. This has led to some people mistakenly thinking some of the animals were escaped domestic pigs. Juvenile animals usually appear first, feeding shoulder-to-shoulder in a tightly knit group, like sheep herded by a shepherd's dog. This is an anti-predator defence, compensating somewhat for their reckless rush at the bait. They do not know that their natural predators, the lynx and wolf, no longer live in the wood: these two carnivores are also extinct from Britain, but irate farmers and fearsome hunters are the predators they can expect. Targeting an animal feeding at a bait station 20 metres away is akin to shooting blue tits on a bag of nuts in the garden. My shots are only with a camera.

The mature animals of the group appear shortly afterwards, when they are sure no danger is apparent. This hesitancy is the reason the animals have lived as long as they have. The mature animals drive off the younger ones who feed on the periphery, in turn displacing the rabbits and badgers who have taken advantage of the free food. Badgers have conceded supremacy of the woodland to the newly established wild boar and keep a discreet distance from them at bait stations. A badger venturing too close is shooed away, but I have never seen a wild boar launch an attack on a badger. Foxes, on the other hand, appear to the boar as a red rag to a bull and are immediately chased away. Maybe the wild boar recognise the fox as a potential predator. Reynard, it seems, has acquired another enemy. I once saw two young boar playfully chase a cock pheasant, the pheasant scampered away followed nonchalantly by the boar. When the pheasant quickened its pace so did the boar until the pheasant legs were going nineteen to the dozen. The boar were just playing and the pheasant only lost its dignity. I have seen magpies perch on the back of a wild boar in the manner of egrets on cattle. The boar was completely nonplussed and probably welcomed the magpies' removal of ticks and parasites. In return, the magpies benefited from a free feed.

Feeding wild boar are permanently nervous and constantly on their guard but the darker the night the more relaxed they appear. They will feed in all weathers but are more skittish when high winds are rushing noisily through the tree tops. A loud bark is their warning sound, issued at perceived or real danger, a rifle shot in the distance or the creaking of a tree in the wind. The bark elicits an immediate response from all the wild boar feeding at the station, usually a dash back to cover. The sound is created by blowing sharply through their snouts and is more accurately described as a snort than a bark. In the eerie silence of the dark woodland it is reminiscent of the air brakes of a lorry being released in a queue of traffic. The sound resonates all around and can send a shiver down my spine if I am walking in the 'no-man's land' between the observation area and my vehicle.

The animals that have dashed back to cover can often be seen standing stock still amongst the trees a short distance away. If the danger materialises a second bark sounds and the animals are gone for good, otherwise they sheepishly creep back to the food and begin feeding again, forever vigilant. The click of the shutter on my camera has frightened a group away on more than one occasion, but if they are not spooked they will feed at a bait station for several hours if there is sufficient food.

The same wild boar will visit a regularly baited station for many consecutive nights. It is difficult to identify individual animals but occasionally a differentiating characteristic, such as a torn ear or bitten tail, can be recognised. Individual animals often approach a bait station from a direction different from the previous night, even though they have spent the day in the same resting area as the day before. Again this is probably anti-predator behaviour. On more than one occasion I have strategically positioned myself to observe the animals more closely than the night before only for them to arrive via a different route that has blown my cover and frightened them off. On these abortive nights I prefer to leave early rather than hope they re-appear, reasoning that if they do return they can feed in peace and will be less wary the following night.

Feeding areas can become scenes of frenzied activity when a group from a neighbouring area arrives. Wild boar approaching a bait station already occupied by a different family group approach cautiously, weighing up the competition. In return, the feeding animals look up and stare at newcomers, ears quizzically pricked forward. The bait station simmers with tension if the incoming group begin to feed. The resident group may attempt to drive off the interlopers and there is much pushing, biting, grunting and loud squealing. With two evenly matched animals the fights look fearsome but victory is mainly achieved by bluff and bravado, serious injury is rare. For an animal whose behaviour is normally so shy and secretive, the noise from these feeding station skirmishes must give away their presence to all and sundry for miles around.

A sow in an alert pose at a bait station in an East Sussex woodland.

During autumn, sows feeding at a bait station may be visited by the hormonally charged males, who are much more interested in the sows than the food. A male wild boar will pursue a sow he suspects may be sexually receptive, constantly champing his jaws together as he does so. This champing action produces the pheromone laden frothy saliva that encourages the sow to mate with him. The noise from his champing can clearly be heard if you are close enough.

In spring piglets can be seen with one or more attendant sows. Piglets, like the adults, have their own hierarchy and play-fight to assert dominance over their siblings. Piglets tend to keep a respectable distance from the feeding adults. I have seen piglets tossed away several feet into the air, by the flick of a sow's snout under their bellies, if they encroach too closely to her while she is feeding. They appear unharmed

Sow in an East Sussex woodland guarding another sow's piglets.

despite frequently landing on their backs and righting themselves with a flurry of leg movements. However, if the piglets get too close to a feeding male, the outcome can be fatal. Like the sow, the male will toss the piglet away with a flick of the snout but the male's tusks can inadvertently catch the piglet, causing a deep and often fatal wound. Piglets inadvertently caught up in a fight between squabbling adults can be trampled or crushed to death. If with regular use a bait station becomes a wet and muddy quagmire, a sow will not feed there if she has piglets. Cold is the biggest cause of piglet mortality and a sow will not risk her piglets getting caked in cold mud and losing too much body heat.

Because wild boar sows in the same family group synchronise farrowing, it is not uncommon to see a single sow with 8 or 10 piglets in a squirming mass about her feet, though they will not all belong to the one sow. The other sow is always close by, hidden from view and watching for danger. This behaviour has led people to erroneously assume that wild boar sows, like domestic pig sows, can give birth to 10 or more piglets at one farrowing. The actual number of piglets per sow averages 4-6 which, the sow will probably agree, is plenty, thank you very much. Wild boar sows are excellent mothers and, more so than domestic pigs, are very aware of their litters and less likely to trample on them. I have on several occasions descended from my lofty vantage point whilst sows and piglets fed below. The first reaction of the piglets when they become aware of my presence was to either to run or crouch down amongst the bluebells and grasses in an attempt to hide. If I trod too close a piglet would ping out in the direction of the sow, who was snorting bad temperedly a short distance away, weighing up the situation. I am told that if a piglet squealed for any reason, then the sow would come running to its aid and I would be charged to the ground. It is not a theory I wish to test.

Watching wild boar, particularly when there are piglets around, is a joy to behold but ethics dictate the needs of the animals must come first. Too many people depositing sacks of bait into the woods may adversely affect the natural behaviour of target and non-target species alike. Because of the risk of spreading disease, meat products, whether shop bought or sourced from a farm, must never be used as bait. Ideally, there will come a day when organised wild boar 'watches', under the guidance of an experienced ranger, are available.

Equally importantly, do not neglect your personal safety. Always carry a mobile phone, map of the area, distress whistle, compass and torch. Do not forget to tell someone where you are going and when you will be back. Woodlands are disorientating enough in daytime let alone at night. More than once I have had to climb a tree to see where the edge of the wood is after becoming lost. Also, when walking in woodland at night tread with all your foot on the ground rather than the usual heel-toe movement. It lessens the chances of you tripping and falling flat on your face.

Finally, be aware they may well be other people creeping about the woodland at night. Some may be up to no good but most are there innocently. I have met, or disturbed, poachers with guns, gypsies setting snares, lepidopterists examining their moth traps, bird watchers listening to nightingales, an embarrassing number of courting couples and once, a man who was looking for the wild boar 'because I've had a bad day at work'. I got the impression he wanted to start an argument with the dominant boar of the area.

4

Biology

Scientific classification

The complete classification of wild boar *Sus scrofa* and an explanation of the scientific terms used are given below.

Kingdom: Animalia.
All animalia are multicellular animals that rely directly or indirectly on other organisms for their nourishment.
Phylum: Chordata
Chordates possess a rudimentary or embryonic spinal column that stiffens the body and supports the movement of the organism
Class: Mammalia
All young mammals are nourished by milk from mammary glands. All mammals possess hair at some stage of their growth development and have three middle ear bones
Order: Artiodactyla
Artiodactyls are hoofed animal with an even number of toes which are symmetrical in shape.
Suborder: Suiformes
Suiformes have a simple stomach arrangement and do not ruminate (chew the cud). The feet usually have 4 toes and the canine teeth often develop into tusks.

Family: Suidae
Genus: Sus (Latin for pig)
Species: Sus scrofa (Wild boar)
The species *Sus scrofa* consists of 16 sub-species

Worldwide, wild boar exist as numerous sub-species. Each sub-species is of similar appearance but has some subtle difference in its morphology, typically small differences in size, coat colour and the shape of the skull bones. The classification of these sub-species is difficult due to inter-breeding between the sub-species and changes in morphology due to local environmental conditions rather than genetics. Wild boar are a favoured animal for hunting and have been introduced into numerous localities and countries for this reason. Some localities may have already supported a wild boar population of their own, so populations are often a genetic mix of different sub-species. The sub-species listed below for wild boar are still being debated and may change as more genetic information becomes becomes available. Included is the range of the sub-species and common English name.

1. *Sus scrofa algira* North African wild boar
Range: Tunisia, Algeria, Morocco and Spanish Sahara

2. *Sus scrofa attila* Middle East wild boar
Range: Romania, Moldavia, Georgia, Iran, Iraq and East Turkey

3. *Sus scrofa baeticus* Andalusian wild boar
Range: Southern Iberian Peninsula

A male wild boar showing the strong shoulder development.

4. *Sus scrofa castilianus* Castilian wild boar
Range: Central and North Iberian Peninsula

5. *Sus scrofa chirodontus* Southern Chinese Wild boar
Range: South China

6. *Sus scrofa coreanus* Korean wild boar
Range: Korean peninsula

7. *Sus scrofa cristatus* Indian wild boar
Range: Pakistan, India, Nepal, East Pakistan and
Bangladesh

8. *Sus scrofa falzfeini* Baltic wild boar
Range: Eastern Poland, Western Russia, Latvia, Lithuania
    and Estonia

9. *Sus scrofa jubatus* Southeast Asian wild boar
Range: Vietnam, Thailand, Laos, Cambodia, Burma and
Malayan peninsula

10. *Sus scrofa leucomystax* Japanese wild boar
Range: Japan and the islands of Honshu, Shikoku and Kyushu

11. *Sus scrofa lybicus* Turkish wild boar
Range: Central and western Turkey, Syria, Lebanon, Jordan
and Israel

12. *Sus scrofa majori* Italian wild boar
Range: Italian peninsula and Italy

13. *Sus scrofa meridionalis* Mediterranean wild boar
Range: Sardinia and Corsica

14. *Sus scrofa moupinensis* Northern Chinese wild boar
Range: China

15. *Sus scrofa nigripes* Central Asian wild boar
Range: Afghanistan, China and Northern Pakistan

16. *Sus scrofa riukiuanus* Ryukyu wild boar
Range: Ryukyu Islands

17. *Sus scrofa scrofa* European wild boar
Range: Germany, France, Belgium, Netherlands, Switzerland,
Austria, western Czechoslovakia, western Poland and
southern Denmark

pure bred wild boar

hybrid wild boar/domestic pig

domestic pig

18. *Sus scrofa sennaariensis* Nile river wild boar
Range: Nile Valley from Sudan to Egypt

19. *Sus scrofa sibiricus* Mongolian wild boar
Range: Mongolia and the mountains of southern Siberia

20. *Sus scrofa taivanus* Taiwanese wild boar
Range: Taiwan

21. *Sus scrofa ussuricus* Siberian wild boar
Range: Manchuria, China, eastern Siberia, Russia

22. *Sus scrofa vittatus* Indonesian wild boar
Range: Sumatra and Java

23. *Sus scrofa zeylonensis* Sri Lankan wild boar
Range: Sri Lanka

Appearance

Wild boar are one of Britain's larger mammals. The weight of a European male boar varies considerably from 50-150 kg and 45-95 kg for a sow. The variation is due to the different sub-species. The smallest animals are found in Mediterranean countries and the largest in East Europe. Body length averages 150 cm for the male and 140 for a sow. The shoulder height of a male can reach 70–90 cm. They are not particularly tall animals but have a stocky muscular build.

The male boar has a body shape that resembles a small buffalo: the head and shoulders are large and the body weight lies forward on the front legs. The animal's back slopes down to small hindquarters and the tail is straight with long tassels of hair at the end. The snout is long and narrow, ending in a cartilaginous disc. The ears are small and always held erect.

Adult males have well developed tusks that grow continually from the age of two. The lower tusks, which have the sharp cutting edge, are continually sharpened by rubbing against the upper tusks which are hollow and act as a permanent whetstone.

Sows are of a similar appearance to the males but have a less pronounced 'buffalo' shape and do not grow tusks. The coat is the same in both sexes, shaggy and brindled with the guard hairs having lighter coloured tips. Beneath the guard hairs is an underlying thick woolly pelage of light brown hair. Both sexes have a mane of longer bristles running the length of the spine. Variations on the depth of brown colour occur in both sexes and range from light fawn colour to almost black. Eastern European animals are generally more uniformly black in colour than western European animals which possess black hairs only on the ears, tail and lower legs.

Piglets are born with a coat of alternating brown and yellow longitudinal stripes. After 12-16 weeks of age, when they are weaned, the stripes are replaced with a reddish-brown coat, resembling the russet colour of a red squirrel. This 'red-phase' coat is replaced by the adult coat on maturity in their second year. Adults annually moult in June-August.

Behaviour

Wild boar are neither gregarious nor solitary animals but lie somewhere in between. They live in highly organised small social groups correctly referred to as 'sounders', but this term is rarely used. The more familiar terms of 'herd' or 'group' are more commonly used. A group of wild boar usually consists of two to five reproductive females with their most recent litters and the surviving young and sub-adults from previous litters. A dominant female leads the

Tusk development in a two-year-old male boar. Note how the upper canine curls upwards.

group and group size varies between 6 and 30 animals. Other group members play the role of teachers, guards and scouts. Different female groups will co-exist in the same areas, sharing favoured resting and feeding areas, but retain their social identity. Mature, unrelated males are found in the vicinity of the female groups only during the rutting season. Male offspring typically leave the maternal group in the early stages of adult life, frequently due to the arrival of a sexually active dominant male in the autumn rut. These sub-adult males may form another group with other displaced sub-adult males. Sub-adult females can also be found with these groups, particularly if hunting pressure has removed the dominant sow, causing the break up of her maternal group. The sub-adult groups break up as the male animals' maturity

Wild boar piglet with characteristic striped coat.

and intolerance to each other grows.

Group structures can change with the coming and going of farrowing females, the emigration of sub-adult males and females (who may re-enter the group at a later stage) and the arrival of unrelated females. Three different social groups can be attributed to wild boar: adult females and their family group, lone adult males and sub-adult groups of mixed sex.

Wild boar are primarily nocturnal animals irrespective of sex, age, or season, although they are more diurnal in times of food shortage or in areas where they are not hunted. A typical day in the life of a wild boar involves one long rest period in dense cover during the day that can last more than 12 hours in high summer. A short period of grooming and wallowing on awakening is followed by 4 to 8 hours' feeding during the night. Nocturnal feeding may be interspersed with a short rest phase. The wild boar's daily cycle of activity is related to the time of sunset. They become active in the last hour of daylight, returning to a secure resting area before sun up.

Outside the breeding season, the mainly solitary males will tolerate the presence of each other around feeding areas but aggression increases in winter with competition for females. The older large tusked males have tremendous strength and little fear of any other animal in the woodland. They are loners said to 'neither seek danger nor avoid it'. During the winter maturing male animals in a sounder are driven away from the group by the dominant males of the area as they are seen as competition for the females. These displaced males form bachelor groups that split when group members fully mature the following autumn.

The area over which a wild boar will range is dependent upon the availability of food, the type of habitat the animal lives in and the sex of the animal - range sizes vary considerably. Males have larger territories than females, the purpose of which is to encompass several female groups. A female's home range is more determined by food and security. Females show a preference for denser and therefore more safe habitats than do males, which spend more time in open habitats. A male's territory can vary from .5-7 sq. miles and a female's .5-3 sq. miles. Within this home range the wild boar often feed at night in a circular or elliptical pattern returning to bed on, or near, the same area as the previous day. The distance covered during a night's foraging varies from 1-9 miles depending on the type of habitat. The home ranges of different groups may overlap if a particular area contains a good food supply or secure resting area.

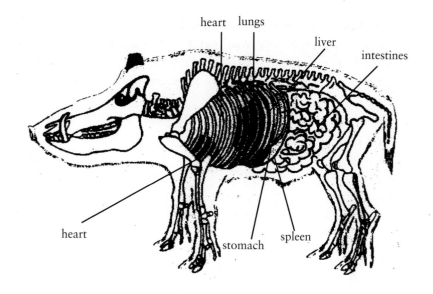

heart lungs

liver

intestines

heart

stomach

spleen

Skeletal structure of a wild boar and the position of the vital organs.

Diet and dentition

The wild boars' preferred habitat is mature deciduous woodland where there is an annual crop of acorns, beech mast, chestnuts or other tree fruits. The highest numbers of wild boar on the Continent are found in woodland ecosystems where forestry operations, such as timber production, do not reduce the autumnal acorn and beech crops. However the species can adapt to different habitats and its omnivorous diet allows it to live, albeit at lower densities, in coniferous forests, alder marshes and reeds. The density of wild boar in Europe is usually below 2 individuals per sq. mile but higher densities occur when supplementary feed is given. Where wild boar shooting is an important source of revenue, they often feed the boar in winter. The artificial feed serves two purposes. Firstly, it ensures sufficient animals survive the winter to

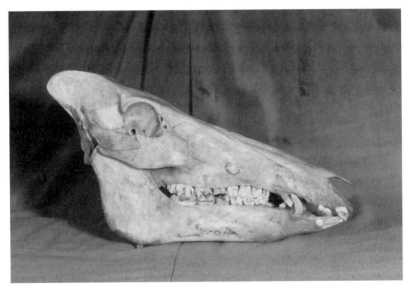

Skull of a male wild boar.(Photos by Will Higgs)

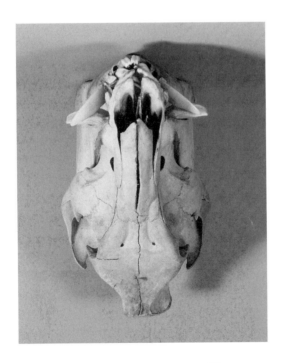

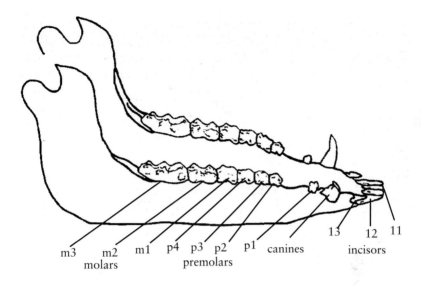

m3   m2   m1   p4 p3 p2   p1   canines   13   12   11
      molars   premolars   incisors

Dentition.

provide sport for the following shooting season and secondly, the feed helps reduce the amount of time the wild boar spend foraging on valuable crops.

The body of the wild boar is adapted to search for food among the surface layers of the soil. Their strong snouts rip through the leaf litter and vegetation, creating bare patches of soil to a depth of 5-15cm. These 'rooted' areas typically compose of several small (less than 1m²) disturbed patches that may overlap. The surrounding vegetation is untouched. Deciduous woodlands have a rich humus layer which the wild boar love to root through in search of bulbs, tubers, roots and invertebrates. The wild boar's diet is predominantly vegetarian but can include insects, worms, larvae, eggs, nestlings, small mammals and carrion. Vertebrate food items such as mice, eggs or nestlings from ground nesting birds are taken opportunistically. Because wild boar are omnivorous, they change their diet to include food that is seasonally abundant. To the annoyance of agricultural producers throughout the world, cereal crops are often eaten in the autumn months when the grain is ripening. Maize and potato fields are also raided. Agricultural damage increases in years of poor natural food supplies, when the wild boar will travel further afield in search of food.

Wild boar have a varied assortment of teeth suited to their omnivorous diet. An adult possesses 44 teeth with the formula: Incisors = 3/3, Canines = 1/1, Premolars = 4/4, Molars = 3/3. Piglets are born with 8 milk teeth, the third incisors and the canines. All milk teeth are acquired by the end of the third month and changed within the second year of life. All permanent teeth are acquired by the end of the second year when the third molar erupts through the gum. The eruption of the molars can be used to determine the age of a wild boar. The continual addition of cement compensates for wear and tear on the surface of the tooth. The eruption of the molars can be used to determine the age of a wild boar. The first molar erupts in the animal's first year of life, the second molar in the second year and the third in the third. The third molar is the largest tooth and has three distinct cusps. The third cusp does not fully erupt until the fourth year of the wild boar's life. Ageing wild boar older than four years by tooth eruption is not possible.

Breeding and dispersal

Sexually active males are found in the vicinity of the sow group only during the breeding season. There is a well defined rutting period in late autumn and winter followed by spring farrowing. In European male wild boar, sexual activity and testosterone production are triggered by decreasing day length and reach a peak in October and November when the rut occurs. During the peak of testosterone production, the sexually obsessed male boar loses interest in his dietary requirements and can lose up to 25% of his body weight. The largest and most dominant males mate with the most females. A male boar will join a sow group, fight off any rivals and drive away the maturing male kin of the group. The odour from pheromones present in the male wild boar's saliva reflects the dominance status of the male as well as stimulating receptivity in the sows. Once all receptive sows have been mated, the boar leaves in search of another sow group within his territory. He has no role to play in the nurturing of his offspring.

Fighting between evenly matched rival males can be fierce and fatal wounds may be inflicted as they attempt to slash each other with their tusks. To lessen the impact of the razor sharp tusks, a protective layer of sub-cutaneous fat forms around the animals' chests and shoulders specifically for the rutting period. The fat is re-absorbed once the rut is over.

A sow born in the spring will first mate in the autumn rut of the following year when she's about 18 months old. She will be in oestrus and receptive to a male with a 21-day cycle from autumn until early summer, at which time she becomes anoestrus until the next autumn. Oestrus is triggered in the autumn primarily by nutritional status and shortening day length. The dominant sow coming into oestrus affects all the other mature sows in the group who come into oestrus also. Synchronised farrowing can then occur between females in the same group allowing opportunities to later cross-suckle another sows' piglets. This clever strategy ensures that in times of want maximum use is made of the available maternal milk supply to aid survival of the group. Another benefit is that all the vulnerable young are together at one time and the appetites of any predators (wolf and lynx for example) are likely to be satiated by this abundant supply of prey. If the farrowing period was more strung out, the numbers of piglets predated would be higher.

Wild boar are seasonal breeders with most piglets born in the spring although breeding can occur in any month of the year. Pregnancy lasts 115-120 days and typically 4-6 piglets are born although sows breeding for the first time often have smaller litters of 2-3 piglets. The ratio of male to female piglets is approximately 1:1. Immediately prior to farrowing the sow leaves the family group and constructs a farrowing nest in a secure area of the woodland. Furthermore, the absence of any other family members, whom she will not tolerate at this time, means her presence will not be betrayed to any potential predators.

Rooting behaviour develops in the piglets as early as the first few days of life and the piglets will follow the sow out of the nest after the second week. In the fourth and fifth weeks she will rejoin the group associating closely with sows that had litters at same time, allowing opportunities for cross-suckling. A sow has 10 teats but to produce 10 piglets in one farrowing would place too great a nutritional burden on her; nature decrees that it is preferable to produce a few healthy young than several sickly ones. However, nature allows the proviso that in years of exceptional food supply a sow can produce a second litter in any one year. A bumper crop of acorns or beech mast will bring the sows into season more quickly and they will conceive at the very start of the autumn rut. Resulting piglets are likely to be born in January and February and are weaned by April. The sow can then be fertilised again before the start of the summer anoestrus period and the second litter would arrive in August or September.

The close proximity to winter means a higher mortality

rate amongst these late born piglets. Competition for food is greater as they are competing with all the young born early in the year and if the previous season's bumper acorn/beech mast crop is not repeated many will not survive. Even worse, if the acorn crop/beech mast crop is poor, mass starvation of young and old animals can occur and population numbers crash. The following spring, the surviving sows are unlikely to breed as their nutritional status is not good enough and population numbers decrease a little more. Not until acorn/ mast crops increase to normal will numbers pick up and the cycle repeats. This is the way of the wild boar, population numbers fluctuating wildly in response to the available food supply.

As an animal population increases, the food supply available in that particular area will decrease. The sub-dominant animals may have to disperse to satisfy their dietary needs or risk starvation. Adult wild boar dispersal strategy is unusual as they may disperse from an area prior to the depletion of the local food resources. This ensures that dispersing animals are physically in good condition and have more chance of finding food in other areas and creating new populations where, as founding fathers, they may no longer be sub-dominant. Dispersal can be of individuals or groups. Animals dispersing are usually adult males or males and females in their second year. Dispersing wild boar from preference will move through natural land rather than cultivated areas, and will skirt around water although they are good swimmers. On the Continent hunting disturbance has, not surprisingly, been shown to trigger dispersal into other areas.

Mortality and predation

Wild boar are a hardy species able to survive in a wide range of climatic conditions. However, snow depth is a critical factor in colder climes: a depth greater than 20 cm prevents rooting and starvation can result. Bad winters in Poland, for example, decimate the local population. A cold snap in spring can prove deadly for piglets. For the first few days of life piglets cannot thermoregulate (maintain their own body temperature) and a sharp ground frost can easily prove fatal. On the other hand, in hot Mediterranean climates, prolonged drought can prove equally fatal.

Hunting accounts for most wild boar fatalities and the older 'trophy' male wild boar with their spectacular tusk growth are particularly sought after. Wild boar can live up to 20 years in captivity although hunting pressures usually ensure a premature death in wild populations where 6 years is a good age to reach.

In many areas of Continental Europe, the extinction of large predator species has meant that the wild boar have little to fear from anything but man. Where predators do still occur in sufficient numbers, for example, in Eastern Europe, wild boar fall prey to lynx and wolves. Both lynx and wolves will hunt red deer and roe deer rather than wild boar, which are more aggressive and frequently found in large groups. Wild boar can actually benefit from the presence of lynx because they feed on deer carcasses left over from a lynx kill. Wild boar are even, if the group is large enough, able to commandeer a fresh kill from a lynx.

5

THE IMPLICATIONS
OF THEIR RETURN

The political and social implications of the wild boars' accidental re-introduction into Britain are many. They impact on a wide spectrum of issues, in particular, agriculture, ecology and conservation. However, the association between this beast and man goes further than just its environmental impact. Wild boar feature prominently in British folklore and heraldry and evoke nostalgic thoughts of the greenwoods from times past. As a 'Royal Beast of the Chase' they hold considerable appeal to members of the hunting fraternity seeking a spirited quarry against which to test their mettle. Should we therefore welcome the wild boars' return and celebrate the rare success of a former native species reclaiming its ancestral habitat? Or is a more cautious approach necessary due to the species' reputation as a fearsome fighter and agricultural pest?

Cultural attitudes worldwide

Tisdell, for his book *Wild pigs: environmental pest or economic resource*, surveyed several countries' governments and found the prevailing attitude to wild boar differed from one country to another. In certain countries the animals are viewed as a pest to be controlled or eradicated, while in others the animals are regarded as an economic resource generating considerable revenue from hunting fees or from the sale of meat. For example, Germany, Poland, Russia, France and Spain all suffer agricultural damage from wild boar but on balance consider the animals to be an economic asset.

Attitudes within a country can be equally varied. In Sweden, hunting associations reportedly want to keep the accidentally re-introduced wild boar, whereas agricultural associations do not. Attitudes can also change: in France, prior to 1970, the wild boar was considered an agricultural pest to be eradicated. This opinion changed after the 1970s when the wild boar was declared a game species and a compensation scheme was set up, funded through hunting fees, to indemnify farmers suffering wild boar crop damage.

In Britain I assessed, in 2002, the media's reaction to the returned wild boar by sifting through every newspaper and magazine article I could find that referred to the wild boar. I found the presence of free-living wild boar in our countryside attracted predominantly negative press coverage: the issues most frequently raised were that the animals constitute a danger to the public, damage agricultural crops, predate livestock and transmit disease. Typical of the media – always reporting the negative side of life! Better news for the boar arrived in 2006 when the government carried out a public consultation and 56.1% of respondents stated they did not want the wild boar populations eradicated.

Public safety

In England, wild boar causing a threat to human safety is officially the concern of the Home Office. A government press release recommended that 'cases involving wild boar where there is a risk to human safety should be reported to the police'. Sightings of free-living wild boar 'where there is no risk to public safety should be reported to the relevant local authority, as they are responsible for ensuring that wild boar are kept in secure

The novelty of a shot wild boar in Kent is deemed to be a newsworthy item.

conditions'. Although wild boar will avoid human contact whenever possible, their fearsome reputation preceded them and it is true that wild boar sows are very protective mothers and, like all good mothers, will defend their young against any perceived threat, including people. But because wild boar spend their daylight hours hidden in thick vegetation, to even glimpse an animal is unusual.

To be attacked by a wild boar without warning is highly unlikely, and if a wild boar is charging at you, all is not necessarily lost. They often dummy-charge, stopping just short of you in a game of bluff that I for one, am content to let the boar win. Captive wild boar are covered by the Dangerous Wild Animals Act 1976, as modified in 2007. Uniquely they are the only free-living species in UK to have this classification bestowed on their captive brethren. Is it therefore safe to walk in the woods where wild boar frequent? Yes, according to Kent County Council who inform in a notice at the entrance to the woodland that wild boar ' ... are not regarded as a danger to the public; however, injured or distressed animals should not be approached.' East Sussex County Council are more wary and display the notice: 'Caution. Wild boar in Woods. Please take care and keep to the path'. These warnings were prompted not by a wild boar incident but following a risk assessment of all potential hazards on council owned land. In these litigious times, it pays to be seen to be showing 'due-diligence' to health and safety issues. In a similar vein, once the wild boar in the Forest of Dean made their presence known, the Forestry Commission swiftly put up signs around their camp sites informing, 'Keep your dog on a lead – Do not feed the boar – Do not approach them – Walk away steadily'.

One area of concern involves people exercising dogs. A dog off its lead running through a wood may scent and disturb a slumbering wild boar and in Britain, dogs have occasionally returned to their owners followed by an angry wild boar, thus compromising the owner's safety. In Germany for example, warning notices are posted around woodlands requesting people to keep dogs on a lead. However, the use of notices warning of potential dangers from wildlife is a double-edged sword. Problems may arise when there is no awareness of the potential danger and people do not alter their behaviour accordingly. On the other hand, panic can be created from over emphasising the minimal risk that wild boar pose to the public.

The request not to feed the boar is a wise one. On the Continent, some wild boars have twigged that in an urban environment they are less likely to be hunted and shot, and people (as people do) even put out food for them. Unfortunately this causes the wild boar to become 'habitualised' and they stay permanently in these urban areas becoming a nuisance by rooting through dustbins, arguing with domestic dogs and wandering in front of traffic. This is occurring a lot, for example, in Berlin, Germany. The wild boar drift into urban areas from the Grunewald park, and as nice as the city of Berlin is, it is not a suitable place for wild boar to roam. The same is happening in Barcelona, Spain, with the wild boar from the neighbouring Collserola Natural Park.

Road traffic accidents

Several wild boar have been killed crossing roads in Britain, particularly where a road dissects two areas of woodland. On one such road there were so many accidents involving wild boar that complaints were made to the District Council demanding action be taken before someone was hurt. To much wry amusement, the council responded by putting up deer warning hazard signs. There were no deer in the area, but the council had no hazard signs depicting wild boar.

All reported accidents are recorded by the police as 'wild animal' and not 'wild boar' incidents. Therefore exactly how many boar have been hit is not known. In common with observations from the Continent, most wild boar in Britain have been run over during the hours of darkness when they move to feeding areas. Their dark coats make them difficult to see, especially on unlit country roads. Wild boar have no road sense and often loiter on the side of the road rooting on the grass verge, making them vulnerable to a collision with a vehicle. On the Continent, seasonal differences have been recorded in the number of wild boar killed on the road with the majority occurring in October, November and December. At this time of year the hours of darkness are greatest, visibility on the roads the worst and male animals are more mobile as it is their rutting season. A similar seasonal trend could be expected for the wild boar in Britain.

Hunting

Wild boar and hunting are closely entwined. In many countries, wild boar are still favoured hunting quarry by groups of amateur hunters or by organised and regulated shoots. Wild boar hunting on the Continent is an expensive and prestigious sport, with hunters killing hundreds of thousands of animals each year in managed hunting forests. The older male 'trophy' boars with their impressive tusk growths are most sought. To preserve stocks, several countries have a close season during the farrowing period when shooting is not allowed.

Wild boar free-living in Britain are currently not protected under the Wildlife and Countryside Act 1981 and are therefore legitimate hunting targets. They have been shot at feeding stations and stalked in open fields under the cover of darkness. Certain local hunters have searched for a secret attractant that will entice the boar more readily to their feed. What substances they are experimenting with cannot even be guessed at; one person lost permission to shoot on a farmer's land after the farmers dog ate the bait put down for the wild boar and was violently ill.

Carcasses are sold locally to game dealers and butchers who have profited from this unexpected business. The meat has good flavour and minimal fat from the boars' entirely natural diet. Combined with its novel appeal, the meat is highly sought after and demand from local hotels and restaurants outstrips supply.

In Britain wild boar shooting is currently an unregulated 'free for all' and animal welfare issues have been raised. For example, the lack of a close season has resulted in lactating sows being shot, which has presumably left unweaned piglets to starve to death. Animals have also been shot at with weapons of inadequate calibre. Carcasses skinned prior to butchering have been found with lead pellets embedded from a previous shooting. This can be a public safety issue. Firstly, a wounded and pained animal may be unduly aggressive and secondly, bullets from the large calibre rifles required to kill a wild boar cleanly are lethal to people at distances measured in miles. In addition, the majority of wild boar have been shot at night when the line of fire behind the target animal is not clearly visible should the shot miss.

Just prior to the banning of handgun ownership in Britain, I spoke to a person who couldn't understand why the police would not give him permission to take his Magnum 44, a canon of a handgun, into the woods to 'finish off any wild boar that I hadn't cleanly killed'.

I knew another farmer who had been asked by a neighbour to shoot a wild boar that had been damaging her fields. The farmer was a 'black-powder' man and an expert in antique firearms. He selected a blunderbuss type weapon, visited the neighbour and took up position in an upstairs bedroom with the window open. As it was getting dark the boar appeared. The farmer loosed off a shot and missed. However, the blast from the muzzle blew out two window panes.

This early animosity towards the wild boar in certain areas was again demonstrated when several farmers and farmhands organised a drive through a Kentish wood where a wild boar was thought to live. I went along to witness if wild boar were actually present for my research purposes. The beaters set off to beat the length of the wood and emerged at the other end over an hour later looking absolutely shattered. In places the wood apparently had been nearly impenetrable and the leather chaps they wore, necessary to protect the legs from bramble thorns, caused them great discomfort in the searing heat of the day. There had been no sign of a boar. 'Shall we go again?' one of guns innocently asked. The language of the replies from the beaters is unprintable.

Public health issues are also raised with the selling of carcasses to butchers and game-dealers. Wild boar carry a heavy parasite and bacteria load from their habit of eating carrion and ingesting soil as they root for food. Several of these parasites and bacterial infections are transmissible to man (known as zoonotic diseases). Shot wild boar in Britain have been butchered and skinned in an unregulated environment and, although it is not known if any disease has occurred from eating the free-living wild boar, the transmission route is already in place.

AGRICULTURAL IMPACT
Crop damage

Worldwide, wild boar are a pest of a variety of agricultural crops. Crop losses attributed to wild boar are high enough for some countries, for example Poland, Italy, France and Luxembourg, to adopt compensation schemes to reimburse farmers. To lessen the economic damage, research has even been conducted into the palatability of certain crop cultivars, such as potatoes, to wild boar. Studies on Continental populations have shown that the severity of wild boar crop damage is related to the autumnal availability of acorns, beech mast and other tree fruits. In years when natural foods abound, less agricultural damage results. Therefore the level of damage attributable to wild boar in Britain is likely to differ from year to year. Similarly, should the wild boar population in Britain increase, a concurrent increase in the level of agricultural damage could be expected. Wild boar have been damaging crops since time immemorial and as long as there are free-living wild boar in Britain, there will be instances of agricultural damage. The challenge in managing the animals is to keep the agricultural damage to a minimum. The farmers' accusation that wild boar follow the drill eating the grain as it falls is not to be taken literally, but as a metaphor is understandable.

In Britain, the farming community was the first to detect the presence of the new wild boar population. Severe damage to pasture land was immediately obvious because the wild boar had ripped up large sods of turf with their snouts in search of roots, grubs and worms. The resulting damage was on occasion quite spectacular.

Because wild boar are predominantly nocturnal, these night-time forays onto pastureland were rarely witnessed. Wild boar were also blamed for cereal crop damage and livestock losses, mainly new born lambs. Evidence of cereal crop damage by wild boar was usually irrefutable but attributing livestock kills to wild boar was less clear cut. Alleged raids were carried out at night and never witnessed. However, if the wild boar were dining out on spring lamb, that is not their usual behaviour. Wild boar will not run down and attack livestock in the manner of a carnivorous predator but they will eat carrion. Thus, if the wild boar were guilty, the most likely scenario was that the lambs were already dead or dying.

The vast majority of sheep kills are still the result of dog attacks. The farmers' own dogs are not exempt. A lady I knew was house sitting for a shepherd who was taking a holiday after a particularly gruelling shearing season. She had to occasionally let his sheep dogs out for some exercise whilst he was away. After three days of being in the kennels they were ready for a run and one dog, completely overcome by excitement, ran to the nearest sheep and promptly savaged it. She didn't let them out again.

However, I can't talk. Whilst searching for signs of wild boar I noticed several sheep in an adjacent field eating

A severely rooted pasture field in East Sussex.

blackberries from a large bramble patch. They were still there the following day, and the day after that. On the fourth day I was accompanied by a farmer and pointed out to him the sheep amongst the brambles, I commented how much they were enjoying the blackberries. He marched over to the sheep and with great difficulty freed them. They were not eating the blackberries, and in fact had probably not eaten for several days, because they were trapped, their woolly coats firmly tangled up in the bramble thorns.

To keep wild boar off his land one farmer went to the trouble of digging in strips of mesh under his fences to prevent the boar rooting underneath. The futility of the exercise became apparent when a boar, disturbed by a tractor, was seen to cleanly jump the fence with several inches to spare.

Vectors of livestock disease

A bigger threat to agricultural livestock interests than allegations of predation comes in the form of transmissible diseases. The recent foot and mouth epidemic in Britain demonstrated all too vividly the harmful economic consequences, and not just to agriculture, of an outbreak of livestock disease. Wild boar have a role to play in this issue as they can carry diseases transmissible to domestic stock. These include foot and mouth, rinderpest, African and classic swine fever and Aujeszky's disease. In Britain, should such a disease become established in the free-living wild boar population, susceptible domestic livestock could be continually infected. Incidents of free-living male wild boar breaking into domestic pig enclosures, inadvertently lured by oestrus sows, have been recorded. The concern is that it is not just their seed they pass on to the domestic sows. The risk of wild boar becoming vectors of this disease during

An attempt to fence out wild boar. Note the mesh is dug down to a depth of 30-40cm.

the outbreak was considered by government vets. Their results were published as a veterinary risk assessment. The assessment noted that 'if Foot and Mouth disease were to be confirmed in an area where feral wild boar herds are known to be present, cage trapping and serological sampling of the boar could be considered as part of the procedure leading to removal of the Infected Area restrictions'. It was stated that 'shooting is likely to increase dispersal (and so spread the risk), and should be avoided if possible'. English Nature also released a press release about the Foot and Mouth disease's impact on wildlife that expressed concern about inadvertently promoting the dispersal of wildlife. It was acknowledged that deer, grey squirrels and hedgehogs can carry the disease as well as wild boar but suggested that control measures 'should be targeted at key species known to be susceptible to disease or likely to carry it significant distances (e.g. wild boar)'.

WOODLAND ECOLOGY
The effect of wild boar on the ecology of British woodland is uncertain. Rooting through the surface layers causes a disturbance regime that will favour some species but not others. Disturbance can eliminate sensitive floral species but also creates opportunities for new individuals to become established, particularly when monocultures of perennial grasses, for example, are rooted. Indeed, a colleague states that 'a woodland without wild boar is a woodland in decline', and I agree whole-heartedly. But away from sound-bites and into science, research is beginning to show the boars' effect on Britain's woodland fauna in a favourable light. Starting below the surface, rooting has been shown to increase leaf litter decomposition and soil nitrate levels, which is good news indeed for plant communities. Furthermore, in rooted areas the dormant

seeds present in the soil layers (known as the seed bank) were triggered to germinate into life. This resulted in greater numbers of individual plants and plant species above the surface than were present previously, showing rooting caused an increase in local plant biodiversity. Again, this is good news for woodland ecology. Staying above the surface, boar rooting has also been demonstrated to reduce the amount of the perennially unpopular bracken which smothers many a woodland floor. Wild boar were also shown to aid seed dispersal because seeds caught in the boar's coat were dispersed when rubbed off during wallowing and scratching on tree bark. In Britain it is worth bearing in mind that plant species diversity within woodland is currently in decline.

The first effect I noticed the wild boar was having on a woodland in southern England concerned a patch of the yellow flowering plant called fleabane. The fleabane was growing in a patch of earth in an area dominated by perennial grasses. The previous winter the wild boar had rooted up some of the grasses to feed on the roots and the fleabane colonised the bare earth. The most striking sight was the large numbers of different butterfly and insect species flying around the flower heads. The wild boar were responsible for turning this dull corner of woodland into a diverse riot of life. Their presence was certainly having an effect on the ecology of this woodland.

Woodland flora

A question often asked is, how will wild boar affect our bluebell woods? Bluebells are synonymous with English woodlands in springtime and are one of Britain's great wild flower spectacles. They abound in the woodlands wild boar frequent in Kent and East Sussex and their bulbs have been rooted up and eaten by the wild boar. Bluebell numbers are currently in decline but it is not known if the wild boar will bring about a further reduction in bluebell numbers. Early scientific results have suggested that individual bluebell numbers were significantly lower in rooted areas than non-rooted areas. However, by the third growing season substantial recovery had taken place and the cover of bluebells was actually greater than prior to the rooting, i.e. there were less bluebell plants in total in rooted areas compared to non-rooted areas, but the plants that were there were bigger in comparison to the bluebell plants in non-rooted areas. The recovery mechanisms are not fully understood but interestingly bluebell plants growing in the rooted area had more seeds, and more viable seeds, per seed capsule than plants in non-rooted areas. I am tempted to add that maybe we underestimate nature's way of controlling ecosystem relationships and, provided boar numbers do not become too great, I doubt if our bluebells will suffer, and may well benefit from being periodically stirred-up.

Of more concern are plant species that have already declined to dangerously low levels, for example, wild daffodils. A host of these golden daffodils seldom occurs 'beside the lake, beneath the trees' as they are now rare in many areas of Britain. They too have been rooted up by the boar and due to their scarcity are more vulnerable to local extinction. It is not certain if the wild boar are targeting the daffodils as the bulbs can often be found left lying on the surface. They may have been dug up only because they were in an area where the wild boar had been searching for fallen chestnuts and acorns.

Thistles are the only plant species I have noticed to survive the rooting experience. Their long taproots anchor the plants so firmly into the ground that they remain standing, like palm trees on an island of bare soil. It is feasible that rooting may locally increase the proportion of thistle plants in an area.

Disturbance can play an important role in maintaining plant communities. In monocultures of perennial plant life disturbed by rooting, the diversity of plant communities has often increased. It is known that wild boar root in specific areas within habitats and often return to previously rooted areas, leaving many areas untouched. Plants that like disturbance will obviously do better in a rooted environment but because rooting is patchy, species sensitive to rooting can survive in the less rooted or non-rooted areas. The intensity of rooting will vary from year to year due to fluctuating boar numbers and natural food supply.

Research on the effect of rooting on tree growth and

Bluebells rooted up by wild boar.

regeneration is also contradictory. Certain studies recorded an increase in growth response to wild boar rooting as a result of improved soil nutrient levels from rooting activity. Other studies have shown rooting to be detrimental to the regeneration of trees and yet another found rooting to have no effect on tree growth. On the beneficial side, wild boar have been shown to have a use as a silviculture tool: they remove competitive weeds and consume the larva of invertebrates considered pests of timber production.

Woodland fauna

Wild boar in British woodland are a 'keystone' species. As a keystone species they are top of the woodlands' food chain. Their general feeding and rooting behaviour can alter the final balance of the woodland's ecology which in turn can affect other woodland species. These effects, felt throughout the woodland, may range from the subtle to the more obvious. It is difficult to predict the effect the wild boars' presence will have on woodland fauna. A wild boar's diet is predominantly vegetarian but can include insects, larvae, eggs, nestlings, small mammals and carrion. However, the vertebrate food items are only taken opportunistically and direct predation on a single species is unlikely. The wild boars' main influence may be as a food competitor, particularly with species that rely on acorns in their diet, for example jays, wood pigeons, squirrels and various small rodents. It has been reported that wild boar will deliberately seek out wood mouse burrows, not to predate the wood mice, but to purloin their acorn stash. The returning wood mouse must be really annoyed.

Discovering how wild boar and badgers co-exist in woodland would be of particular interest. Both species are opportunistic, have a similar omnivorous diet, rootle through leaf litter and are predominantly nocturnal. Incidentally, wild boar and badgers share one other trait ominous to cattle farmers, both are known to carry bovine TB.

The difficulty in predicting the effects of rooting

One of the problems of studying the effect of wild boar on woodland flora and fauna is the fluctuating size of a wild boar population. Wild boar numbers vary considerably from year to year according to the available food supply, in particular acorns and beech mast. Because these food items naturally vary from year to year so will wild boar population numbers. Further fluctuations in wild boar numbers and consequently rooting density would come from disease, hunting pressure, predation and climatic conditions. Fluctuating population numbers mean that the ecological effects of rooting disturbance on the woodland floor will not be consistent from year to year.

In Britain, the wild boar have created a disturbance regime the woodland has not experienced since the species extinction several hundred years earlier. Rooting up the soil and consuming insects, plants and small mammals alters the woodland ecology in many ways. For example, wild boar in a Polish forest consumed in one year 59 species of plants associated with forests or meadows, and 45 species of invertebrates. If the wild boar had a similarly varied diet in woodlands in Britain, there would be an ecological knock-on effect throughout the food chain. For example, one of the woodlands in southern England is home to the silver-washed fritillary. This uncommon butterfly lays its eggs on tree bark close to patches of dog violet. The caterpillars descend from the tree trunk to feed on the violets. It is not known if the apparent increase in violets in rooted areas will benefit this butterfly or if their numbers are limited by other factors.

There are no definitive answers to the question of how wild boars rooting will effect the woodland ecology, only a few pointers from recent research in Britain and a few clues from research carried out on the Continent. For thousands of years wild boar were an integral piece in the jigsaw of our woodland ecology, but the jigsaw box is lost and how the completed picture should look is unknown.

6

THE FUTURE

Exotic invader or a returning native species?

Should the free-living wild boar in Britain be considered the fortuitous accidental re-introduction of a lost native species or the unfortunate re-introduction an exotic invader (a species entering a region where it was previously absent)? The obvious answer to this question is that they are the re-introduction of a lost native species. However, when considering a species' re-introduction into ancestral habitat nothing is that simple and there is a set of guidelines, devised by International Nature Conservation bodies, that first needs to be satisfied, before determining if a species is a suitable candidate for re-introduction. The purpose of the guideline criteria is straightforward – to prevent an introduced species from damaging the endemic flora and fauna.

In Britain, there are several cases where an introduced species has proved detrimental to established native species. For example, grey squirrels from America were deliberately released into the wild towards the end of the 19th century and are now common throughout most of England, Wales and lowland Scotland. Despite their engaging antics, their habit of stripping bark from trees has made them an economically significant pest of forestry. They also predate an unknown number of nestlings and have been implicated in the demise of our native red squirrel populations. Mink provide another example. The first record of escaped mink breeding out of captivity in Britain was 1956. Today they are found throughout the country and are strongly implicated in the drastic decline of the water vole population, their main prey item. A third example is muntjac, a small deer native to south east Asia. Muntjac first escaped from captivity at the turn of the century and now occur in woods and copses throughout most of southern England and South Wales. Muntjac affect woodland ecosystems by eating the shoots of young trees and rare woodland plants such as orchids.

Prior to the deliberate re-introduction of any species, a feasibility study is necessary to assess socio-economic concerns, environmental impact and future management techniques. The feasibility of re-introducing wild boar into Britain, to reinstate a species whose extinction in historical times was solely due to man, has been discussed by conservationists. Forested areas of Scotland were mooted as possible release sites. However, discussions were only at an early stage and no official feasibility study had been commissioned. Meanwhile, as the discussions were going on, the wild boar sneaked in through a back door at the bottom of England and quietly established themselves.

Applying guideline criteria

To decide retrospectively if the free-living wild boar would have been suitable candidates for re-introduction into Britain, the guideline criteria used by international conservation bodies can belatedly be applied. The wild boar satisfied the following main requirements:

(i) There is a clear understanding of why the species was lost to this country
- habitat loss and over hunting at the hand of man.
(ii) There are suitable habitats of sufficient extent and isolation to which the species can be re-introduced
- the wild boar have already chosen their preferred woodlands

(iii) Their loss does not prejudice the survival of the population from which they are taken
- wild boar numbers on the Continent are currently increasing
(iv) To re-establish keystone species
- in Britain, wild boar are a keystone species
(v) To increase or maintain biodiversity
- Britain's biodiversity has now been increased by one
(vi) Provide economic benefit to local people
- local revenue has been generated from the sale of carcasses to game dealers

But they failed on one crucial issue:

(vii) The individual animals taken for re-introduction are genetically as close as possible to that of native populations.

The sticking point in deciding if the wild boar running around Britain were suitable candidates for re-introduction is their genetic make-up. There are two genetic issues, purity of the breed and the type of sub-species.

1. GENETIC PURITY

Why might the wild boar not be pure?
Some, but not all, wild boar farmers in the UK cross pure wild boar males with domestic pig sows to produce an increase in litter size, from an average of 5 in pure animals to 9 in hybrids. More frequent farrowing, to twice yearly, also occurs. This 'hybrid vigour' obviously makes economic sense. Domestic Tamworth sows are often used, the resulting young being known as 'iron-age' pigs. If the free-living wild

boar originated from one of these farms then the animals at large might be pure, hybrid or a mixture of both. Because the type of establishment the free-living wild boar originated from is not known for certain, only anecdotal evidence can be used to guess their genetic purity. The Dorset animals may be pure as they are thought to have originated from a now defunct wild boar farm whose stock was registered as pure bred with the British Wild Boar Association. Although registration does not guarantee that animals are genetically pure, it is the most reliable system available to association members.

The Kent and East Sussex population is less straightforward. If they are from the wild boar farm they are alleged to have escaped from in the storm of 1987, they too may be pure as the owners claimed all their stock was 100% pure-bred wild boar. No clues exist about the wild boar said to have escaped from the abattoir in Ashford, Kent.

Hybrid animals that contain only a small amount of domestic blood will still have the same physical appearance of pure wild boar, so a lack of purity may not be important from an aesthetic point of view. However, it would be of relevance to a management programme, since the greater fecundity of hybrid sows will influence the rate at which the population will spread into new areas.

How can you tell if a wild boar is pure bred?

Currently it is not possible to differentiate between pure-bred and hybrid animals using blood chemistry or genetic tests. Genetic material from one animal can be compared to another and differences in the material noted, but this does not tell if one of the animals is pure bred, only that there are differences. There are no definitive standard samples of 'pure' wild boar against which unknown samples can be compared.

It can not be known for certain if standard samples of 'pure' wild boar are actually pure. The reason for the doubt is due to:

1. Historical cross-breeding with escaped or free-ranged domestic pigs many centuries ago.

2. Recent contamination of pure bred populations from the movement of animals from different regions or countries to re-stock areas over-hunted the year before.

3. Wild boar populations, genetically the same but in different localities, gradually changing in shape and appearance in response to environmental factors, known as 'environmental plasticity'.

4. Wild boar having many different sub-species that have never been definitively classified.

Why not use chromosome numbers?

The French, who take wild boar farming and hunting very seriously as big money is involved, have wrestled with the problem of purity for years. Their solution is to use chromosome numbers. French wild boar have 36 sets of chromosomes whereas domestic pigs have 38 and hybrids 37. Therefore an animal that looks like a wild boar but does not have 36 sets of chromosomes is not pure. Unfortunately things are not so cut and dried outside of France. 'Pure' wild boar in areas of Eastern Europe also have 38 chromosomes and wild boar with 36, 37 and 38 chromosomes can appear spontaneously in all areas. British farmers have imported Eastern European animals as farm stock and therefore several different groups of chromosome numbers are likely to be present in the free-living British animals.

How is purity currently determined (aside from chromosome numbers)?

Purity is judged on an animal's shape and appearance. Below are listed the typical characteristics of a pure wild boar and a hybrid.

Pure wild boar characteristics

Head is narrow with a straight profile.
Snout is narrow, straight and long.
Muzzle is always black.
Ears are pointed and held erect.
Tail is straight with long tassels at the end.
Hind quarters are sloped and the shoulders (esp. in males) are large.
Body weight lies forward.
Legs are long.
Coat colour is brindled and an underlying brown pelage is present.
Piglets have brown and cream stripes.

Hybrid characteristics

Head is broad with a concave profile.
The snout is short.
Muzzle is often marked with pink.
Ears are broad and slightly pendulous.
Tail more or less corkscrew.
Coat splashed with white.
Light coloured hooves.
Upper line of body straight.

To the untrained eye these differences are not that easy to

distinguish, especially if the animal contains only a small amount of domestic blood. However, to simplify, characteristics that almost certainly indicate hybridisation are: floppy ears; pink noses or feet; curly tails; white socks; white areas on body; spots; saddles or other splodges of colours in the coat; dished nose.

2. SUB-SPECIES

The second issue that prevents the wild boar being classed as a native re-introduction concerns the type of sub-species present in Britain. No one knows what sub-species of wild boar Britain originally had, therefore no direct match is possible. However, it can reasonably be assumed that the original British animals were similar to the French since the British and French land masses were once joined. The sub-species found in France is *Sus scrofa scrofa*. If we assume the original British animals were *Sus scrofa scrofa*, then what sub-species are the free-living animals currently in Britain?

It is known the original British farm stock was predominantly of French origin but as the industry expanded farmers supplemented the original stock with animals of both west European and East European origin. No separate records were kept by the authorities on which countries wild boar were imported from as they were all banded together with domestic pigs. The only records available have been compiled by the now defunct British Wild Boar Association (BWBA) in a herdbook for the benefit of their members. These records are not definitive as the origin of many animals was unknown and not all wild boar farms or other establishments housing wild boar are members of the BWBA. However, the herdbook gives an indication of the origins, and hence sub-species, of the animals held in Britain. The herdbook shows that animals

Wild-type coat.

from several countries are present in Britain, although the majority of countries lie within the range of the sub-species *Sus scrofa scrofa* and *Sus scrofa falzfeini*. Using guideline criteria west European animals (*Sus scrofa scrofa*) would qualify as a re-introduction because they are the nearest extant European relatives to the extinct UK sub-species, but East European animals (*Sus scrofa ussuricus*) would not.

To sum up, Britain has a melting-pot of wild boar of unknown purity and consisting of an unknown number of sub-species. Further additions to the genetic pool of the two British populations, which may already contain genetically mixed and even hybridised animals, are possible, since future escapes of captive wild boar cannot be ruled out. However, no free-living wild boar in Britain have been reported with any characteristics that could be associated with being

Pale-coloured coat.

Comparison of the two colours

hybrids except that a pale-coated variety exists in the East Sussex population. These pale-coated animals have no other characteristics to imply that they are hybrids and the pale coats may just be natural variation, as wild boar coat colours do vary considerably.

DEFRA attempted to solve the purity issue once and for all by comparing free-living British wild boar DNA with samples from Continental boar and domestic pig breeds. Their much awaited conclusion: 'Overall, the results were inconclusive'. DNA analyses showed that British boar were within the range of variation of Continental wild boar populations. DNA analysis also showed that British boar are most closely related to Dutch and French boar and were not especially distinct from the European populations examined.

The importance of the genetic purity of the wild boar boils down to personal taste. If you are against the wild boars' re-introduction, the uncertainty over purity may offer a ready-made excuse to try and eradicate them. If you are for their re-introduction, purity is not such an important issue because the animals look and behave like pure wild boar. Considering many wild boar populations on the Continent are not 100% pure, due to out-breeding with escaped hybrid or domestic animals, maybe we should not get to concerned about purity.

Conclusion

The feasibility of re-introducing wild boar into Britain, to reinstate a species whose extinction in historical times was solely due to man, was being discussed by conservationists. Forested areas of Scotland were mooted as possible release sites. However, discussions were only at an early stage and no official feasibility study had been commissioned. Meanwhile, as the discussions were going on, the wild boar sneaked in through a back door at the bottom of England and quietly established. Re-introduction discussions among conservationists changed to management discussions among civil servants. Civil servants, as they are apt to do, discussed the matter considerably, and then some more. Meanwhile, boar continued to escape, or be deliberately released, setting up new populations in several other counties and countries (e.g. Wales and Scotland). Finally, Natural England (which is part of DEFRA) could contain themselves no longer and released their position statement:

'In recent years several small populations of wild boar have become established in England. The wild boar is a former native species and arguably the most significant vertebrate introduction/re-introduction since the European rabbit. Presented with this fait accompli the Wildlife Management & Licensing Service has been working with the Evidence team to develop a Natural England position on this important species.

'Following a recent Policy Strategy Group meeting the proposed policy position has been adopted. This recognises feral wild boar as a former native species which can contribute to Natural England's objectives for the conservation and enhancement of the natural environment. However, it also recognises that they have the potential to spread some livestock diseases and can cause damage to agriculture and other interests. We therefore encourage their positive management and favour a regional approach, where they are removed in areas where their impact would be unacceptable, but are managed sustainably elsewhere. Natural England will continue to monitor the development of these populations and, where appropriate, their impact on other wildlife and habitats.'

It was a long time coming.

References

1. Yalden, D.W. (1999) *The History of British Mammals* (T. & A.D. Poyser, London)
2. Anon (1991) 'Bear leaves 'em all baffled', *Kentish Express*, 3 January 1991
3. Goulding, M.J., Smith, G. & Baker, S.J. (1998) 'Current status and potential impact of Wild Boar (*Sus scrofa*) in the English countryside: A risk assessment'. Central Science Laboratory report to the Ministry of Food, Fisheries and Agriculture.
4. Mayer, J.J. & Lehr Brisbin, I. (1991) *Wild pigs of the United States. Their history, morphology and current status*(University of Georgia Press,Georgia)
5. Tisdell, C.A. (1982) *Wild pigs: environmental pest or economic resource* (Pergamon Press, Sydney)
6. Goulding, M.J. & Roper, T.J. (2002) 'Press responses to the presence of free-living wild boar (*Sus scrofa*) in southern England'. *Mammal Review*, 32, 272 - 282.
7. DEFRA (2006) Wild boar consultation analysis of responses published. News release Ref: 239/06, 29 May 2006. http://www.defra.gov.uk/news/2006/060529a.htm (accessed 26 Nov 2007).
8. DEFRA (2001) 'What is the risk of feral wild boar becoming infected with FMD and subsequently causing new incidents of FMD in domestic livestock?' DEFRA Veterinary risk assessment No. 7, 11 June 2001.
9. EN (2001) 'Foot and Mouth disease - impact on wildlife'. English Nature press release EN/01/08, 2 March 2001.
10. Sims, N.K.E. (2005) 'The ecological impacts of wild boar rooting in East Sussex'. D.Phil. Thesis. University of Sussex.
11. 'Trees for life. Update on the Guisachan Wild Boar Project' (2006) http://www.treesforlife.org.uk/forest/missing/guisachan200611.html (accessed 26 Nov 2007).
12. Welander, J. (2000) 'Spatial and Temporal Dynamics of a Disturbance Regime: Wild boar (*Sus scrofa L.*) rooting and its effects on plant species diversity'. PhD Thesis, Swedish University of Agricultural Sciences, Utgivningsort.
13. Stubbs, D. (1988) *Towards an introduction policy: conservation guidelines for the introduction and re-introduction of living organisms into the wild in Great Britain*. Wildlife Link, London.
14. DEFRA (2004) *The Ecology and Management of Wild boar in southern England*. http://www.defra.gov.uk/science/project_data/DocumentLibrary/VC0325/VC0325_2113_FRP.doc (accessed 26 Nov 2007).
15. Natural England (2007) 'Meeting Scoping document: Developing Natural England's Policy Position on Feral Wild Boar'. Natural England, UK.

Index

If you have enjoyed this book, you might be interested in other titles published by us. Some of these are:

BATS Phil Richardson paperback £7.99
BADGERS Michael Clark hardback £9.99
BEAVERS Andrew Kitchener hardback £9.99
FROGS & TOADS Trevor Beebee paperback £7.99
GARDEN CREEPY CRAWLIES Michael Chinery hardback £11.99
The New HEDGEHOG Book Pat Morris hardback £12.99
MAMMAL DETECTIVE Rob Strachan paperback £7.99
OWLS Chris Mead paperback £7.99
POND LIFE Trevor Beebee hardback £9.99
SEALS Sheila Anderson hardback £9.99
SQUIRRELS Jessica Holm paperback £7.99

FOXWATCHING Martin Hemmington paperback £7.99
SPIDERS Michael Chinery hardback £9.99
THE STATE OF THE NATIONS' BIRDS Chris Mead paperback £12.99
SEAWEED Sonia Surey Gent and Gordon Morris paperback £12.99

We charge £2.50 for postage and packing if you wish to order a book. Alternatively they may be purchased from any good bookshop. If you would like a catalogue of all our titles, please write to: Whittet Books Ltd, South House, Yatesbury Manor, Yatesbury, Wiltshire SN11 8YE.